The People's Friend

Friend

2024 Annual

Mourne Mountains, County Down

It sounds like a clue in TV's fiendish quiz "Only Connect": what's the link between Percy Bysshe, the Black Stairs, Pigeon Rock and Butter Mountain? The last name might put you on the right track – they're all to be found in the Mourne Mountains in Northern Ireland.

It's not just the names that are picturesque. This is an Area of Outstanding Natural Beauty, which attracts tourists from all over. Some come for the climbing – Northern Ireland's highest mountain, Slieve Donard (850 m), is here – while others appreciate the amazing views as well as the range of activities and attractions in the region. Of course, some visitors may well be drawn by the fact that this is the site of many locations in the cult HBO series "Game Of Thrones".

Yet even before the dragons of Westeros were a tiny gleam in author George R.R. Martin's eye, the legends of these granite peaks and valleys inspired the young Belfast-born C.S. Lewis. He populated them in his imagination with Lucy, Edmund, the White Witch, Aslan and all our other favourites from his classic children's series, "The Chronicles Of Narnia". Truly a fantastic landscape.

Contents

Dear Readers . . .

Welcome to "The People's Friend" Annual 2024! We've filled its pages with a whole year's worth of great reading to entertain, uplift and inspire you.

Inside you'll find 25 brand-new short stories written specially for us by some of our favourite "Friend" authors, and 11 delightful poems to enjoy. We take a look at the facts and folklore surrounding the much-loved birds to be found in Britain's beautiful gardens and countryside, and share a selection of J. Campbell Kerr's stunning watercolour paintings of locations around the UK.

Angela

Angela Gilchrist, Editor

p135

The Perfect Resolution

by Eirin Thompson

DOROTHY was good at resolutions – she had buckets of resolve.

One January she'd decided to lose two stones, and she'd succeeded by the middle of August.

Another year, she'd promised herself she'd read a new book every month and she'd stuck to that, too – everything from John le Carré to "Bridget Jones".

She'd decluttered, changed to decaff, taken advanced driving lessons and joined an exercise class.

Never once had she shrugged her shoulders in February and decided it was too much trouble.

"You must be pretty near perfect by now," her friend, Wanda, commented, as New Year came around again.

"There can't be anything left for you to do."

Dorothy sipped her coffee and smiled.

"I wouldn't say 'perfect', exactly, but I am going to give myself a break this year."

"What, no new resolutions?"

"I didn't say that. I'm moving on to George. This year, it's going to be all about him."

George was Dorothy's son.

He had returned home to live with her 18 months ago after his long-term relationship with Eva broke up.

Wanda eyed Dorothy dubiously.

"You can't make George the object of one of your famous resolutions," she warned.

"Of course I can!" Dorothy shot back.

"He's been moping about for a year and a half, and no sign of a date, much less a girlfriend.

"My New Year resolution is to find him a new partner."

"Have you told him about this?" Wanda wondered.

"I don't think telling him would be advantageous," Dorothy replied. "Mum's the word."

∗   ∗   ∗   ∗

Dorothy decided that the first thing to do was to kit George out with some new clothes.

"Nicholson's is the place to go," she ordered on Saturday morning, as George ate his breakfast, protesting that his mother had got him out of bed much too early for the weekend.

"You can pick up some nice casuals and a new suit."

George was just opening his mouth to object when they both heard tuneful whistling at the back door.

"That'll be Jack," Dorothy said.

"Who's Jack?" George enquired.

"Really — you might know if you got up a bit earlier. Jack brings all our fruit and veg for the week. I'd better go and pay.

"Give me your bowl and I'll pop it in the dishwasher. You run upstairs and get ready for our shopping trip."

As George retreated upstairs, Dorothy called up after him.

"And make sure there aren't any holes in your socks!"

Although Dorothy thought George would find some nice clothes in Nicholson's, she had an ulterior motive, too, in taking him there.

The gents' department wasn't only staffed by men – there was also a very attractive young woman of around George's age, and she didn't wear a wedding band or an engagement ring.

Dorothy had made it her business to notice.

When they arrived at menswear on the first floor, Dorothy didn't take long to spot the young woman, who was straightening a rack of shirts.

Dorothy linked arms with George and marched him across the floor, before dropping his arm and coughing politely.

The young woman turned round.

"Hello. I wonder if you can help us," Dorothy began. "My son's looking for a complete new wardrobe."

"Oh – a new look for the new year!" the young woman said, smiling. "Were you hoping to find something in our sale, or did you want to see our new season's stock?"

"Oh, the new stock, I think," Dorothy replied, then realised that she should be letting George do the talking. "I mean, that's what you said, George – isn't it?"

George smiled weakly.

"I'm not quite sure what I want – I was rather hoping you'd give me some advice."

Dorothy pondered – did that make him seem ineffectual, not knowing his own mind?

Or would a woman his age relish this as an opportunity to style George to her own sartorial taste?

"I'll just sit on the chair over there and let you young people work it out," she said.

From a distance, she watched as George popped in and out from behind the changing room curtain.

Please don't step out in your boxers and socks, she willed him.

But he didn't let her down, preserving his modesty at all times, chatting and smiling with the pretty assistant.

Dorothy found herself crossing her fingers.

Was it possible that today, on the very first day of her resolution, George might find himself with a date?

They were at the counter now, the assistant placing garments into the stylish Nicholson's carrier bags and ringing them up on the till, George selecting his card for payment.

Dorothy couldn't resist bobbing over.

"Well, how did you get on?" she asked.

"Very well," George replied. "Lisa was a great help."

"And George was easy to fit," Lisa replied. "Tall and slim, so he won't need to have anything altered."

So they were on first-name terms, Dorothy noted with glee. Plus Lisa had noticed George's build.

Surreptitiously, Dorothy pressed her foot down on George's toes.

Well, say something, George, she willed. Ask the girl out for a drink!

But all George said was, "That's my foot you're grinding into the carpet, Mum — do you mind?"

"I was telling George he's the same size as my boyfriend, so I had a pretty good idea what would fit," Lisa piped up.

"I say 'boyfriend', but really it's fiancé, now — Brian popped the question on Christmas Day. We're picking out a ring in the sales."

Dorothy's heart sank.

Engaged on Christmas Day — George was a week too late.

Still, it had been optimistic to expect a resolution to be fulfilled on the very first day.

At least now George had some very nice clothes with which to impress the next candidate.

$$* \quad * \quad * \quad *$$

Dorothy insisted they go home so George could change into one of his new outfits, and then she would treat them to lunch at the Green Olive.

"What's the occasion?" George asked.

"I don't need an excuse to take my son to lunch!" Dorothy declared.

Secretly, she was hoping they might find themselves near a table of eligible young women, or in the care of an attractive waitress.

When George appeared downstairs in his new navy chinos and chunky cardigan, Dorothy thought he looked awfully well.

"That Lisa's done a good job," she said, deciding to forgive her for being engaged.

"Well, if I pass muster, let's get moving," George replied. "I'm starving."

The Green Olive was an appealing venue, in the style of a conservatory, with lots of light, space and potted plants.

The tables were draped in crisp white linen and laid with weighty cutlery and large sparkling glasses.

Dorothy and George had arrived a little ahead of the lunchtime crowd, and the waiter proposed a table on its own.

Dorothy hesitated.

Over by the window was a table of three young women, talking animatedly — it would suit her purposes much better to be close to them.

"Could I put in a special request for that little table for two by the potted palm?" she asked innocently.

"I just have some very happy memories of that particular spot . . ."

She let her voice trail off wistfully, and the waiter, though surprised at anyone wanting that spot so near the doors to the kitchen, complied.

It wasn't enough just to be near the young women — Dorothy had to ensure that George actually got noticed.

"Good afternoon," she said, stopping at their table. "And may I wish you all a Happy New Year.

"Gosh, your salads look delicious. I was thinking of fish, but a nice

fresh salad might be just the thing after all the excesses of the season.

"I'm Dorothy, and this is my son, George.

"Of course, George can eat what he likes and never puts on weight.

"I suppose that's because he swims and works out — he keeps his metabolism at a good rate."

Dorothy felt the young women staring at her, then looking at each other with some puzzlement.

She'd laid it on too thick, hadn't she? She shouldn't have crashed their girlie lunch and made such a full-on speech.

She might as well have written *Available* across her son's forehead.

"I'll leave you to enjoy your lunch in peace," she whispered, and groped for her chair.

Fortunately, George didn't seem to have noticed anything, as he'd headed straight for the menu.

He jumped up now, and tucked his mother in at the table.

"There's a seafood chowder I like the sound of," he said.

Dorothy had one eye on the menu and the other on the waiting staff.

Counting Blessings

We need a little cheerfulness
Whatever comes along,
We need a ray of hopefulness
If things are going wrong.
The many simple things in life
Are so important, too,
A comfy chair, a cosy bed,
Just right for me and you.
A loving word, a friendly call
Can have a happy touch,
Don't ever take for granted
The things which mean so much.
As we go forward week by week,
Let's make another start,
For counting blessings every day
Can lift and warm the heart!

Iris Hesselden.

There were two men and one woman, all young.

She was hoping it would be the woman who attended their table.

After a moment, the young waitress approached their table and Dorothy whooped inwardly.

This time, she must resist the temptation to go for the hard sell.

George was nice-looking, and his new clothes were smart and stylish. Let him speak for himself.

The waitress took their order and poured them each a glass of water.

When she returned with their starters, Dorothy couldn't resist testing the situation with a little remark about the demanding hours of working in hospitality and how it must be tricky to carry on a social life.

The waitress smiled charmingly at both of them.

She explained that the best way to make it work was to have a relationship with someone in the same industry — someone who understood.

Hence, she had married the Green Olive chef.

"I don't wear a wedding ring," she explained, seeing Dorothy looking.

She winked at George.

"Not since the time it fell off into the soup!"

* * * *

Dorothy knew it had been a good day − a successful shopping trip, a delicious lunch − but as they walked back to George's car, she couldn't help feeling disappointed.

Her resolution about fixing up George with a new woman had got nowhere.

Look at that lovely estate car of his − it was a car for a family man.

It should be full of a wife and kids and shopping.

"You feeling OK, Mum?" George enquired as they drove home.

"Just a bit tired," Dorothy replied.

As they took the shortcut through Atkins Avenue, they came on a blue van by the side of the road, belching smoke.

"Someone's in trouble. We should stop," George proposed.

Dorothy's heart sank as George flicked on his indicator and pulled in.

Of course it was admirable that George saw someone in need and wanted to help, but she could have done without this.

But, glancing in the mirror, she saw a woolly-hatted figure standing by the van, kicking the nearest wheel in apparent frustration.

"Oh! I know who that is!" she cried. "It's Jack, who delivers our fruit and veg."

"Well, you sit tight, Mum − it's starting to rain. I'll see what I can do."

Two minutes later, George was back.

"I'm going to take you home first, so you can put your feet up, then I've offered to come back for Jack.

"There are still eight more deliveries to complete, and I've said we can use my car − the boot's certainly big enough.

"Jack reckons the van can wait until the customers are looked after."

* * * *

Dorothy only meant to lie down for 20 minutes, but she must have fallen asleep on top of the bed and when she awoke it was dark outside.

She looked at the clock. Half past seven!

She checked her phone. There was one message − it was from George.

All deliveries successful. Towed Jack's van to the mechanic's place and then helped her close up the shop. She's grabbing a quick shower and then we're going for tapas and drinks. Don't wait up.

Dorothy smiled.

Jack − Jacqueline − the fruit and veg girl.

She was young, friendly, totally down to earth and apparently single.

Turned out George hadn't needed his mum to make a resolution about his love-life.

Once he was ready − and it was understandable that he required his own time to get over Eva − he was perfectly capable of sorting that out for himself.

Wait until Dorothy told Wanda! ∎

Inveraray, Argyll And Bute

On the shores of Loch Fyne, the longest sea loch in Scotland, lies Inveraray, the traditional county town of Argyll in the heart of Campbell country. Inveraray Castle, the seat of the Dukes of Argyll, heads of the Clan Campbell, looks out over the loch. If the gracious lines look familiar, it could be because the castle was based on a drawing by Vanburgh, the eighteenth-century architect of Blenheim Palace and Castle Howard.

The third Duke replaced an older version of the castle, which had stood since the 1400s. Work began in 1746 and the building took 43 years to complete. To go with the new castle, the Duke undertook to design a completely new town to replace the old village of Inveraray. Though William Adam drew up the plans in 1747, most of the design and building work took place between 1772 and 1899.

13

Out On The Moors

by Shona Partridge

EMILY remembered the day in late summer when they'd made their decision to move here.

Standing on top of Whin Tor you could see for miles, the neat fields with their drystone walls laid out below them like a toy farm.

"I wish we could stay here for ever," she'd said. "I wish we didn't have to go back to London tomorrow."

Mark was silent for a moment as he put his arm round her shoulder.

"What if we could stay here for ever? Seriously, we could. There's a farm just along the road from here that's up for sale. We could afford it with the sale of the London house."

Emily could tell Mark was being serious.

"We've always talked about getting out of the city. Well, this could be our chance. If not now, when? What do you think?"

"Oh, Mark, it would mean so much! And this one here could grow up in the countryside with fresh air and open spaces." She patted her slight baby bump with affection.

Emily watched a hawk as it hovered above their heads.

It let out a piercing cry that seemed to encompass all the wildness of the heights. To live among this landscape every day would be heaven.

*　　*　　*　　*

The low building made Emily think of "Wuthering Heights". The old, mellow stone had darkened with the years and the leaded windows appeared to be original. There were even roses growing round the porch door.

Emily could make out an old carved inscription above the lintel.
The Whins, 1682, Montague.

They loved the old-fashioned interior just as much, with its huge carved fireplaces and stone-flagged floors.

What had started as a whim became something very real as they

Illustration by Sailesh Thakrar.

wandered through the rooms and imagined the nursery they would set up in the small south-facing room next to what would be their own bedroom.

"Is it just me, Mark, or does it feel like the house is very welcoming?" Emily asked as they paused on the landing.

"No, not just you, Em. I'm feeling it, too."

Emily was reminded that her engineer husband had an imaginative, sensitive side.

Two months later they got the keys and took ownership of their new home.

Emily stayed behind, with her parents' help, to complete the move out of the London house.

Mark was all set to do a bit of organising and painting before Emily moved north.

*　　*　　*　　*

"I've got us a sheepdog, Em."

Emily could hear the smile in Mark's voice over the phone.

"And you'll never guess what his name is. It's just perfect. You're going to love this, Em."

Mark was silent for a long moment – so long that Emily wondered if they had lost the phone connection.

"Mark?" she asked.

"Oh, sorry, Em." Mark put on a deep voice and announced, "Our new hound rejoices in the name of Heathcliff."

Then he laughed.

"I kid you not! You'll meet the splendid fellow at the weekend. I just sent you a photo, have a look.

"He's lying by the stove right now. I think he's in charge of the house and farm. He certainly thinks he is. He was the farm dog here before the last owners. He belongs here.

"And he's a proper black and white Border collie," Mark went on. "You'll love him, although he tells me he's a serious working dog, not a pet by any means."

"So that'll be why he has the prime place in front of the Aga, then?" Emily said as the photo appeared on her phone.

She laughed. It was perfect.

"I can just see myself," she said, "going to the door of our very own Wuthering Heights and calling for our dog. Heathcliff! Heathcliff, come home!"

Their shared laughter seemed to shrink the miles between them.

The dog's name and history felt like wonderful happenstance, almost an omen for their new life on the hill farm.

*   *   *   *

Emily closed the door of the London house for the last time.

She could hardly wait for the train to hurry north to Mark and the Whins.

The removal van would be there before her and Mark would set up what suitable furniture they had.

In time they would get some more appropriate, hopefully antique, furniture, but for now their eclectic mix of family heirlooms and modern oak would have to serve.

Emily was most looking forward to setting up the nursery. Mark was painting it yellow.

She took the picture of the scan out of her purse. This little person would soon be a reality out in the world.

*   *   *   *

"This was run as a small sheep farm and I want to give it a try, Em," Mark said not long after they had settled in. "What do you think? We have the land and access to hill grazing, too. It feels right to me. These lands have run sheep since the Middle Ages."

Emily agreed and they both found themselves reading up on hill farming.

In what spare time he had, Mark apprenticed himself to Ronald Burdis – known to everyone as Rusty, on account of his red hair.

"These hill sheep are really hardy, and you can run them as free range and even organic. I'll keep you right. You'll get some additional income from the wool, too.

"Not much to start with, but the main thing to do initially is build up your flock and learn the ropes," Rusty told Mark.

It was an all-weather outdoor job, but Mark loved that aspect and felt ready to take on a small flock in the late autumn. Not the best time, but they had to start somewhere.

The snow came deep and early that first year at the Whins.

Emily and Mark hunkered down by their own fireside, dreaming of the future and planning for the new baby. Emily knew real contentment in their new home.

Their newfound idyll was broken late one winter evening.

It started with Heathcliff.

Emily noticed he was unsettled, shifting on the hearth rug and looking about the room nervously. Then he began a disturbing whine that gave her chills.

The atmosphere in the room shifted and the temperature seemed to drop. Heathcliff let out a low growl as he stared intently at the window.

Emily followed his gaze and let out a cry of shock. There was a face staring in, a white-faced girl with tangled hair plastered against her head by the wet snow.

"Mark!" she cried out. "There's someone at the window!"

But the face had already vanished.

"I'm scared, Mark," she admitted. "I really did see someone, and Heathcliff did, too."

"I believe you, Em. I hope no-one is in trouble, but we'll need to go out and check."

Minutes later they were outside in the whirling snow with their torches, checking round the house and in the outbuildings. But there was not a sign of any girl.

"Well, there's nothing else we can do tonight," Mark said eventually. "Let's go back inside before you catch a chill."

It was only after they had gone back inside and bolted the door against the snowy night that it struck Emily.

She had seen no other footprints in the snow.

*　　*　　*　　*

Now, Emily always made sure the curtains were drawn before full dark. Even so, she couldn't help imagining that pale face against the glass.

Another night they were about to go upstairs when they heard a door slam and what sounded like running feet on the landing.

"It's an old house prone to draughts and strange noises," Mark rationalised.

Emily and Mark settled into the community, making new friends.

One evening they went to a local history event at the village pub.

"This song is variously known as 'Lord Gregory', 'Gregory Of The Whins' or 'Fair Emily'. Tonight, I'm singing this song for the new residents at the Whins. Unlike this song, may their story have a happy ending!"

The singer told the story behind the song as he tuned his guitar.

"There is a secret marriage and a child, but the girl is not welcomed by her new husband's family. She is banished by her own family for marrying beneath her, and when she goes to the Whins, Gregory

Spring Angels

I thought I heard a cuckoo call
Somewhere in the trees;
I'm sure the air is sweeter now
More gentle, on the breeze.
There's a wonderful awakening
Of magic, on the wing;
We look about for birthing signs,
The joy, in everything.
Then all at once we see them there,
Little lambs frolicking free,
Pretty slender bluebells
The sweet crocus, heavenly.
The scent of golden daffodils
Flooding the woodland floor,
The creatures with spring fever:
This time which we adore.
The birds fly high, in the powder blue,
The rainbow, reflecting praise.
Nature has sent her spring angels
To delight with new glorious days.

Dorothy McGregor.

Montague's mother says he is away from home and refuses to let her in. She is lost in the snow with her poor bairn.

"Here's the song . . ."

It was all too much for Emily.

Hearing such a sad tale about her own home and the tragedy that befell a young mother made her feel sick and lightheaded.

She slipped from her chair in a dead faint.

She came round almost at once to find Mark fussing over her.

"I'm all right, honestly," she assured him. "It's just a shock to find this out after the weird things that have been happening. We knew nothing about the tales and the history, yet we have experienced such odd events."

"Surely you knew?" Rusty asked. "Did no-one tell you the story of the house before you bought it? Its history is bound into the traditions of this area.

"People do claim to have seen Gregory and Emily near the house in the winter, and a girl's face at the window."

"Well," Mark replied, turning his beer glass absently, leaving wet circles on the dark table top, "we bought it through an agent and they saw to the viewing and us getting the keys. We just loved it at first sight. "We knew it was late seventeenth-century because of the carving above the door. The brochure said as much, but with no hint of a haunting or any specific historical information.

"Come to think of it, the background was rather vague. I should have asked more questions," he admitted.

"Anyone living around here could have told you the tale. I'm surprised they didn't, really," Rusty continued. "I'm wondering if the sellers had a bad experience and wanted out. They were only there for eighteen months. They never became part of the community.

"The family before them were the original farming stock for generations. Your Heathcliff was their dog before they emigrated to be nearer their family.

"From what I know, people of the Montague name owned the original farm and built the house."

* * * *

There was heavy snow forecast and Emily knew she'd need to get the sheep down from the hill and into the fold.

Some of the ewes were nearly ready for lambing, so they needed to be close to the farmstead.

Mark was in town on business, but it would only take her and Heathcliff about an hour and a half.

It was only midday, so there was plenty of daylight left.

"Come on, Heathcliff. We're off up the hill to take the sheep home. Come on, boy."

Heathcliff looked at her intently with his head to one side.

He barked in agreement, heading at once to the porch, where Emily got into her outdoor gear and heavy boots.

She still felt a bit pretentious taking her shepherd's crook, but this was no mere affectation.

The crook really did help her get up the hill faster. It helped her balance and avoid dangerous peat hags and rabbit holes.

Soon they were nearing the rough hill grazing, where their 20 ewes spent most of their time.

Emily had brought a little feed to help coax them down.

Besides, good old Heathcliff was a prize-winning sheepdog, known for his speed and efficiency in getting sheep into the fold. They could do this together.

Feeling almost like a professional shepherdess, Emily called instructions to Heathcliff.

He hardly needed to be told, gathering the straggling flock, ready to be ushered downhill to the farm.

"I don't like the look of that sky, do you, Heathcliff?" Emily said, looking at the yellow snow-clouds racing towards them from the hilltops. "You go home with the flock and I'll catch you up." Emily had got a stitch and wanted to slow down.

There were only seven weeks left till her due date and she knew that going out on the hill would have to stop for now.

Still, they had done a good job together, she and faithful Heathcliff.

She watched the dog, sleek as a wolf, keeping the flock together as they trotted off down the hill before him.

"Good boy. Good boy, Heathcliff," she called after him. "Home! Home, Heathcliff!"

At first there were only a few feathery flakes, spiralling down from that leaden sky.

But soon even the sky was blotted out in a whirl of thick snow.

An icy wind began to blow the snow directly into Emily's face till she could barely see her way.

Very quickly the ground was covered and, in the gusts of wind, small drifts started to form.

Within minutes the heavy snow had become a driving blizzard and Emily fought to stay upright, more glad than ever before of her shepherd's crook.

It was less than a mile to the farm, but soon Emily had lost her way. It was unbelievable how much snow could fall in 20 minutes.

Everything looked the same in the white-out, when she wasn't even able to see more than a mere yard in front of her.

She had tried her phone, but there was no signal up here in the storm.

She ploughed on through the drifts, thinking only of home and of keeping her baby safe.

If only I'd kept Heathcliff with me, she thought desperately. I could have followed him home.

Emily wasn't sure any more if she was walking in a straight line or in a circle, as she seemed to be making no headway.

As the snow grew deeper it became harder to walk, despite the shepherd's crook.

She could feel her strength ebbing as she trudged on, becoming colder and colder.

She fell in drifts a couple of times, struggling out of the snow, feeling winded. Then she fell more heavily in a particularly deep drift. This time she didn't get up.

Somewhere in the distance she was sure she could hear someone calling her name.

"Emily! Emily!" The voice carried over the storm.

Then she saw a shape coming towards her through the falling snow.

"You must get up," the stranger called out. "Stand up, or you and your babe will surely die out here. Follow me and I will see you safe."

Emily managed to stand and wondered in her dazed state why the man did not bother to help her up.

He kept a couple of paces in front of her so Emily did not see his face.

Somehow, they found their way back to the crossroads and the big drystone wall that marked the boundary of the hill grazing.

The wall could be followed all the way back to the Whins.

Then Emily realised she was alone again. Whoever her helper was, he had vanished.

By now the wind had died down and the snow had finally stopped falling.

She could see the way ahead, and there, running towards her like a rocket, was Heathcliff, barking joyfully as he began to run in circles around her.

Behind him were Mark and Rusty.

"Oh, Emily! I thought I'd lost you. Don't ever do that to me again." Mark gathered her close in his arms. "Now, we're carrying you back to the house. Don't even think of walking another step."

* * * *

When they were safely back at home in dry clothes, nursing hot drinks, Mark told her how he had come to the rescue.

"I can't explain it, Emily. I just got this overwhelming feeling you were in danger. Then I couldn't raise you on the phone and I had to get home.

"Fortunately, I got back before the roads were blocked. Heathcliff was there, waiting for me, as if he expected me. He was fairly frantic, so I called Rusty to help and we followed good old Heathcliff till he found you."

"What about the man who helped me, Mark? I want to thank him for leading me out of the snowdrifts and back on to the road home."

"There was no-one else, Em. I saw only you. You must have dreamed it when you passed out."

The more Emily thought about the experience over the next few days, the more convinced she became that it was Gregory who had helped her.

"Have you noticed how quiet it's been round here since you rescued me from the snowstorm?" she asked.

"Maybe you really did see Gregory," Mark replied.

"I feel sure he helped me, Mark. Maybe he's at peace now that he has saved someone, when he couldn't save his own Emily and her child. It almost feels like the balance has been restored."

* * * *

Emily and Mark decided to call their new son Gregory.

When he was older, Gregory would be told the story of the snowstorm and the dramatic rescue that had led to his naming.

The first time Emily took Gregory out to the garden in his pram for some spring sunshine, she was surprised to see people on the hillock at the back of the house.

There, standing between the elms, was a man with his arm round a young woman who was holding a baby.

As Emily looked, they seemed to dissolve into the air, and soon it was as if they had never been there at all. ■

In The Dog House

by Becca Robin

I T can be tricky when a new child joins a school later in the year. It's bewildering at first, with so much to learn about their new environment, and we hope that they will soon make friends.

At St Faro's, where I am head teacher, we pride ourselves on taking time to help a new child settle in. This was the case at the start of the spring term when Andy joined Miss Okoro's class of five-year-olds.

His family had just moved back to the UK following several years in France, where Andy's parents had been working.

On their initial visit, Andy seemed very shy. When we took him to the classroom to meet the children, he hung back.

His mum explained about his imaginary friend, a large St Bernard dog named Watson, who joined the family shortly before they'd left France.

It wasn't a surprise when Andy turned up on the first day of term and told his teacher, in a small voice, that Watson had come with him to school.

It was the only thing Andy did say that day, besides answering when his name was called for the register.

He joined in tentatively with the activities, wrote his name when asked and drew a picture of himself and Watson playing in their garden.

I knew Janey Okoro would do her best to pair him up with chatty children, but Andy wasn't ready to talk. This went on for a few days, before he slowly began opening up a bit more.

Even though I have been at the school for so many years, our "Signs of Spring" topic never fails to enchant me.

Spring is such a joyous time, with the natural world returning to life after a long winter. As teachers, we see young children encountering the phenomenon for the first time, and it's a privilege to appreciate the changes through their eyes.

Lots of children had been bringing in nature items they'd found on their way to school for the display table outside Miss Okoro's room.

There was a beautiful collection of catkins and pussy willows, as well

as books showing illustrations of hatching chicks and leaping lambs.

One morning, I walked down the corridor to find the table in complete disarray, with the vases overturned and books knocked over.

Not only that, further along the corridor, all the children's coats, which normally hung on pegs, were lying in an untidy heap upon the floor.

"Children." I stood in the doorway of the classroom and clapped my hands to gain their attention. "There's a terrible mess in the corridor and – oh! Our poor 'Signs of Spring' display. Whoever made that mess?"

At first the children were quiet, then one child chirped up,

"I think it was Andy."

Andy looked up from where he was playing with construction toys on the carpet, and shook his head vehemently.

"It wasn't me," he said in a very clear voice. "Watson did it."

"Well, maybe you'd like to help Watson clear it up again," I said. "Together with a few friends."

I selected a couple of helpful volunteers who trooped out with Andy to tidy up the mess.

It wasn't the first of Watson's acts of rebellion.

A few days later the class made chocolate crispy cakes, but when I went to admire the finished results, I found the children sitting in silence and a stern look on Miss Okoro's face.

"I'm sorry, Mrs Williams," she said. "We're trying to find out who sneaked in at breaktime and took three of our cakes from this plate."

Casting my eye over the children, I spotted the chocolatey ring around

Andy's mouth.

"Watson did it!" he piped up when he caught me looking at him.

Soon Watson was becoming the bane of our lives, and for a while I wasn't sure how to approach the problem.

Telling Andy we didn't believe in his imaginary friend seemed the wrong way to go. I spoke to his mother, who was apologetic, and said she didn't feel her little boy had completely settled at our school yet.

As St Faro's is an inner-city school, we always arrange plenty of visits to our local city farm. A trip had been organised for Miss Okoro's class to see the lambs that had been born recently.

The children did lots of stimulating preparatory work.

They listened to stories, painted pictures of lambs and wrote sentences about what they wanted to see at the farm.

Andy was as enthusiastic as all the others.

An idea came to me for what we could do about Watson.

On the morning of the trip, when the coach drew up outside the school, I caught up with Andy.

"Andy," I began in a gentle voice. "The farm has rung to say dogs aren't allowed, because they might scare the lambs. Watson will be bored if he is left on the coach. He can stay in my office while you go on the trip. I'll even take him for a walk at lunchtime."

Without getting into much of a discussion about it, I led Andy along to my office, where I had put a cushion on the floor.

Hesitantly, he led Watson to the cushion.

"Oh, my goodness! Quick, it's time to go!" I exclaimed.

I waved the children off on the coach and noted that Andy didn't look too worried.

He had settled into a seat next to a lovely boy named Fariq, and they were chatting away excitedly.

I rang Janey Okoro on her mobile at lunchtime to make sure all was well.

"They're having a great time," she said. "They've petted the lambs and seen chicks hatching. The children have been so well behaved. You'd be proud of them."

"Everyone?" I asked.

"Oh, yes," Janey assured me. "Andy's been with Fariq all day. The two of them are getting on famously. How's Watson?"

"Quiet for the time being," I replied. "Let's hope it stays that way."

"When we get back to school, should I send Andy to the office?"

"No," I replied. "Let's wait and see what happens."

The children returned at half past two, tired out but thoroughly content.

I peeped through the classroom door and saw them sitting on the carpet with a biscuit and a drink of milk, watching a DVD as a treat.

Andy was still sitting happily with Fariq. He seemed to have forgotten all about his imaginary friend.

Andy turned a corner that day. The two boys are still firm friends and Watson has remained in my office ever since! ▪

Blue Tit

ONE bird that you're likely to see in your garden – as well as in woodlands and hedgerows – is the blue tit.

With a blue crown and vibrant yellow breast, with touches of green, too, it adds a welcome splash of colour to the garden.

Each female bird usually produces anything between eight and a dozen eggs, which are laid one a day.

Once hatched, that means a lot of hungry mouths to feed, especially as each chick can consume around 100 caterpillars daily!

Blue tits also enjoy spiders, insects, seeds and nuts.

They will make use of garden nest boxes, lining them with moss and feathers for extra warmth. Providing boxes is a great way to encourage blue tits into your garden.

Treat them to sunflower seeds and fat balls (removing the net first) when food is in short supply in the winter months. ■

Driving Me Nuts

by Kate Hogan

Y OU'VE gone too far this time, Joseph," I said, staring at him, flat on his back under what was left of the apple tree, which had crashed through the conservatory.

"I'm ringing an ambulance," I added, while wondering if they'd send the men in white coats for the two of us.

"No," Joseph squeaked. "I'm OK. Just help me up, Norma. The roof might cave in."

I teetered backwards, surveying the damage.

The apple tree seemed to be groaning, as if, like me, it couldn't take any more.

I didn't blame it. Not one bit.

* * * *

"It's costing us a fortune," I'd said a year ago, not long after Joseph decided that early retirement made this the time to get back in touch with nature.

"How many types of seed can a bird eat? What's wrong with throwing out a few crusts like they used to do in the old days?" I'd asked.

He'd waved the "Birds In Your Back Garden" hardback he'd ordered from the internet.

"Different birds like different food," he said, eyes gleaming.

"Some thrive on Niger seed, some like sunflower seed, some like . . ."

"You're spending at least fifty pounds a month," I said.

"And that's not even counting the money you're spending on all these fancy bird feeders hanging everywhere.

"Which – by the way – nearly knock me out every time I try to hang the washing out."

I pointed to the fading bruise on my forehead.

"Couldn't we plan to get back to nature at a nice little hotel by the sea or something? It's my retirement, too, you know."

Illustration by Shutterstock.

He wasn't listening.

"Men go a bit funny in the head when they retire," my sister said.

"Look at my Jim's sudden desire to put shelves and cupboards up everywhere.

"Best leave them to it. It's only a hobby – no harm."

Well, a few shelves and cupboards wouldn't be so bad.

In fact, our home was full of DIY projects that he'd been promising to complete for years.

But I was banging my head on swinging bird feeders every time I stepped out the back door – that was what I would call "harm".

Tripping over the wires from Joseph's ridiculous bird-box camera systems wasn't much fun, either.

"We're endangering ourselves with all this paraphernalia you're ordering online," I pleaded.

"But we can watch the babies being born," he said enthusiastically.

"Look – I've rigged everything up so we can watch it all on the little portable TV in the dining-room."

"I don't remember you being in such a rush to watch our babies being born," I said with a sniff.

"In fact, Joseph, I vaguely remember you fainting and having to be put into a side ward."

"You'll love it, Norma," he said, probably not hearing a word I'd said.

But before long, I'd almost become used to the garden being like some kind of assault course, and in fairness, Joseph was right.

The garden was soon filled with birds I'd never seen before: goldfinches, bullfinches, greenfinches and more.

Despite myself, I did love seeing all the wildlife.

I was watching the delightful birds in awe one evening when I saw two squirrels doing fancy two-steps and gymnastics along the branches of our apple tree, before hurling themselves on to the bird feeders.

I laughed out loud at their antics.

"Joseph!" I shouted, thinking he'd be delighted.

"Tell me it's a nuthatch," he said, nearly knocking me over.

"Squirrels," I said, pointing excitedly as the bottom of one of the feeders gave way under a herculean wrench from one of the squirrels.

I watched, fascinated, as the nuts cascaded out all over the lawn.

"Aren't they funny, love?" I asked.

My husband didn't say a word, but rushed to the door.

From the patio, Joseph started what appeared to be some sort of Highland Fling, with lots of strange roaring vocalisations.

I don't know what the neighbours thought, but the squirrels were none too impressed and scarpered up the apple tree in seconds.

"Are you really that excited?" I asked when he came back inside.

He looked at me darkly.

"Got to get rid of 'em," he said.

I frowned at him.

"But they're nice. Fluffy. We've never had squirrels in the garden before . . ."

But he was staring at the broken bird feeder with such concentration it could have been the Lost Ark.

"Got to get rid," he repeated.

Maybe if his Highland dancing had done the trick and scared the squirrels off for good, things wouldn't have got so bad.

Of course, it didn't work.

Every day the squirrels came back – and they brought reinforcements.

More squirrels and new plans, destroying bird feeders and all before them.

Joseph was determined to beat them. He spent hours concocting ways to protect his feeders from the fluffy-tailed invaders.

At first it was a bit of wire here . . . a bit of glue there.

Squirrels dealt with those efforts without much of a thought, managing to rip the bird feeders and covering the garden with seeds and nuts.

Joseph ran around like a headless chicken, mock-threatening them with an old rake.

Then I got up in the early hours one night, thinking there was someone creeping about the garden.

There was. Joseph!

I watched him with a creeping feeling of dismay.

He was inserting wire hangers in all sorts of strange places so the squirrels couldn't get through to the nuts.

Then And Now

The music, as we drive along,
Recalls those teenage days,
And memories now come flooding back
As each cherished pop song plays.

Sixty-seven, the summer of love,
With flowers in our hair;
This music that they're playing now
Reminds us we were there.

Things can change as years pass by
Whilst other things may stay,
Such as, for us, that flower power
As evidenced today.

I'm switching off the radio
As we reach the garden centre;
We feel a sense of childish joy
As, hand in hand, we enter.

Our hair may not be long and sleek,
Our movements not so fast
But the pleasure that the flowers bring
Has lived on from that past.

John Darley.

By morning the garden looked as if we'd been invaded by creatures from outer space. I saw the thoughtful looks on the squirrels' faces before they took on the challenge and met it.

Even Joseph running around screaming with the rake had no effect on them now.

They obviously thought it was some kind of entertainment Joseph was putting on for them, but I'd started getting very strange looks from the neighbours!

"Joseph," I said one morning, as he was skulking round the garden, grey and haggard after being up all night. "We really need to talk.

"Why have you nailed all the lids from my pans on the smashed-up bird feeders?

"There are hardly any birds to feed. The garden's a sodden nut and seed infested mess.

"You've got to give this up or I'm leaving. You've gone mad, Joseph. You're stalking round like a crazed man. You hardly recognise me.

"You don't talk to me. You just give me these strange chilly stares, while you think of your next manoeuvre to beat the squirrels. You . . ."

"That's it!" Joseph said, as if I didn't exist. "Chilli – chilli powder!" He slapped his own head.

"Squirrels hate it. How had I forgotten?"

That was when I took myself into the bedroom to pack a case and book a last-minute weekend away by the sea, to get us both away from the madness!

An hour later, after hearing an almighty crash from outside, I was staring at the wreckage of our marriage, and our home.

"Ambulance is on its way," I finally said after explaining the sorry story to the operator.

✳   ✳   ✳   ✳

"I wasn't even injured, Norma," Joseph whimpered when the paramedics had left.

"It wasn't blood, Norma, it was chilli powder. I made a paste and painted the apple tree branches.

"I must have just been a bit heavy on that last branch. The one the squirrels . . ."

"So you're really not injured, Joseph?" I asked. "But you will be – seriously – if the garden isn't back to the way it used to be when I get back.

"And now, look! The conservatory needs sorting, too.

"I don't want to see another bird feeder in my life! E-mail me with the pictures when it's done."

I picked up my case from the hall and headed outside to the car.

"But Norma!" he shouted. "Where are you going?"

"Leaving," I said, as I headed towards the door.

Maybe I'd stay at the little B&B by the sea, then start a new life.

"Please don't leave me, Norma. I love you. It's only a hobby.

"I know I've been acting crazy, but what with early retirement, I've just been trying to keep occupied!

"But I'll change. I'll stop all this bird stuff. Take you wherever you'd like to go, if we can go anywhere. Nothing's worth anything without you."

I felt an unexpected surge as tears pricked my eyes. Joseph loved me!

I guess I'd known he did, but it had been a while since he'd uttered those three important little words. I stared at his sad face.

I thought of how much I'd started to love the birds, too. I didn't want them disappearing from our garden.

I didn't want Joseph, mad as he was, disappearing from my life, either!

"How about a cup of tea and we'll talk about our plans?" I asked, but Joseph already had his arms around me, and that was more than good enough for me! ■

Arbroath, Angus

Lying on the north-east coast, some 15 miles north of Dundee, the town of Arbroath has some big claims to fame.

It's been a popular dwelling spot for centuries; archaeological finds in the area date back to the Iron Age. By 1178 the little fishing village was important enough to acquire its own abbey, founded by King William the Lion in memory of his friend Thomas Becket, the assassinated archbishop of Canterbury.

In 1320, the abbot was influential in the production of the Declaration of Arbroath. This famous letter to Pope John XXII asserted Scottish independence and asked him to recognise Robert the Bruce as the rightful King of the people of Scotland.

After the abbey fell into disuse following the Reformation, it was used as a source of handy construction material for local buildings.

Its ruin still forms an impressive structure and is cared for by Historic Scotland.

Arbroath isn't just pretty – if you like hot-smoked haddock, the Arbroath Smokie, a local delicacy, has been prepared in the traditional way over open wood fires around the harbour for centuries.

That fishing trade was helped by another of the town's claims to fame – the Bell Rock Lighthouse, one of Stevenson's original structures, built on the Bell Rock in the North Sea in 1807. It is now the oldest sea-washed lighthouse in the world.

Every Trick In The Book

by Liz Filleul

T HE number of burglaries in this area gets bigger every week," Dad grumbled, jabbing the "Police Round-up" column of the local newspaper in disgust. "People will soon be afraid to go out." "I don't know what the world's coming to." Mum leaned across our scrubbed wooden table to refill Dad's cup of tea.

"People used to be able to leave their doors unlocked. Nobody stole anything.

"Do you want more tea, Geri?" She angled the teapot over my cup.

I checked the clock. Fifteen minutes till I had to leave.

"Just a half cup, please. I don't want to miss the bus."

I was four days into my first week in my first job.

"Listen to this." Dad cleared his throat before reading out a paragraph from "The Keysborough Gazette".

"*Jewellery worth more than three hundred pounds was stolen from the home of Miss Romola Kendrick in Hollies Road last weekend.*

"*Police found that a window had been forced open and believe the theft took place between Friday night and Saturday afternoon. The jewellery, including a sapphire brooch, earrings and a gold pearl ring, was taken from the main bedroom.*"

Romola Kendrick. It was a name straight out of adventure stories involving plucky heroines. I'd loved books like that as a child, and still sneaked a read of them even now I'd turned fifteen and finished school.

"*Four hundred pounds in notes stolen from the home of Norman Edwards in Avenue Road, Clinton Marby.*" Dad frowned.

Clinton Marby was the next village to ours. He sighed heavily and turned the page.

I swallowed the rest of my tea.

"I'd better run."

I started work at nine, and while there was a bus that got me to Keysborough at ten to nine, I preferred to catch the one that got me there at half-past eight rather than risk being late.

Illustration by Gerard Fay.

An hour later, I jumped off the bus and made my way along the high street, along with all the other commuters who worked in the shops.

Thursday was early closing day in Keysborough, so we'd all be finished by one o'clock.

I window-shopped as I walked, thinking of what I might buy with my first week's wages.

I had to give Mum and Dad some board, and I was going to the pictures on Saturday with friends, but maybe I could buy a lipstick, or the latest Elvis single. Should I save up for some shoes or a bolero jacket?

It was super finally to be earning a living.

Although I hadn't liked school, I'd always loved reading, and had liked the idea of working in a bookshop or library, so I'd been delighted to get a job as a bookshop assistant at Fine Print Second-hand Bookshop.

Now, as I rounded the corner, I noticed Fine Print's lights were on. Mr Johnson was already here. I didn't need to wait for the shop to open.

Through the mullioned windows, I could see him behind the counter, already talking to a customer, even though it was only quarter to nine.

The door jangled as I opened it, and Mr Johnson's head jerked up from the box of books he was riffling through. I spotted a flicker of annoyance cross his face when he recognised me.

"You're early, Miss Russell. I'm busy, so have a cup of tea out the back. Once I've finished with my customer, I'll organise some work for you."

Mr Johnson was in his sixties, with receding grey hair and glasses. He

33

always wore three-piece suits that looked like they dated from the 1920s.

The customer couldn't have been more different. He looked about eighteen, had blond hair styled like Elvis Presley's and wore a rust-coloured suede bomber jacket.

He grinned and winked at me, and I blushed and scurried past.

The bookshop itself consisted of one large room where most of the books were shelved, and a smaller one to the side, where children's books were kept.

At the back of the shop was a poky kitchen, and next to it a large office/storeroom, where Mr Johnson did all the administrative work and sorted out the books he purchased.

He stored any valuable books in the office, to be sold to collectors or at auction. The others were sold in the bookshop at reasonable prices.

"I want the books sold, not sitting on the shelves for ever," he'd told me on my first day.

I hung my gabardine mac on the hat stand and poured a cup of tea from the pot.

"Belonged to your aunt, you say?" I could hear Mr Johnson asking.

"Yes, that's right. Me and Ma are trying to clear her house out. Ma was all for chucking them in the bin, but I said no, let's see if we can get a bob or two for them."

"A bob or two's all I can give you, I'm afraid . . ."

I heard the ding of the cash register, and shortly after that the sound of the front door opening and closing.

A moment later, Mr Johnson carried the box of books into the office.

"When you've finished your tea, there's a pile of books behind the counter ready for shelving. I'll make a start on working through these books. Call me if the shop gets busy or if a customer has a question you can't answer."

I glowed inside, thrilled that he trusted me to handle customers by myself already.

The work wasn't hard. Mr Johnson had taught me how to operate the cash register, and to enter details in the sales book on the counter.

He had a second book for acquisitions, where he recorded the price he'd paid for the books.

In the case of the rarer books, the price was a lot less than he sold them for. I'd been surprised when he'd told me how much some books were worth.

I finished my tea, and started working my way through the pile of books behind the counter.

The first few were children's books, so I carried them into the children's room. I made room on the B shelves for the Enid Blytons – a couple of Famous Fives, plus a Malory Towers book.

It had been my love of the Famous Five, and the character George in particular, that had led me at the age of eight to abbreviate my name from Geraldine to Geri, and now everybody called me that.

Well, everybody apart from Mr Johnson!

Half of the remaining books were detective novels: several Agatha

Christies, a couple of Margery Allinghams and a handful by authors I'd never heard of.

By my fourth day, I already knew that Agatha Christies were quickly snapped up by customers.

That was a shame, as I'd have liked to read some of them before they disappeared from the shop!

I'd just finished shelving the books when the door opened and two elderly ladies stepped inside, making a beeline for the murder mystery shelves.

Within 15 minutes, the Agatha Christies had been sold.

*   *   *   *

All those months when I'd been longing to leave school, Dad had warned me that I'd miss it once I started working.

"No more finishing at four o'clock," he'd said, "and no long school holidays or half-terms."

Well, he was wrong. I much preferred working to being at school.

Finishing at five o'clock and having the evening free was much better than walking home from school at four with a satchel crammed with homework.

And it was smashing having spending money, too.

The only thing I wasn't keen on was that I had to work Saturday mornings. The only full day I had off was Sunday, and my Saturday and Thursday afternoons were free.

Still, I was enjoying the job.

During my first six weeks, Mr Johnson took advantage of quieter periods to teach me some tricks of the second-hand book trade. He told me which authors, books and editions I should keep an eye out for.

"You never know, you might spot one of these at a market or church jumble sale for just a few pennies," he told me.

He often came across valuable books that way himself.

Sometimes he'd emerge from his office beaming over finding a valuable book among a box of otherwise cheap stock.

At school, I'd daydreamed about working in a modern bookshop, but I was becoming interested in rare books. Perhaps one day I'd have my own second-hand bookshop. I could specialise in children's books.

"I want to have my own record shop," my friend Pat told me one Sunday. She'd left school at the same time as me, and worked in a record shop on the other side of Keysborough.

"Then I can play records I like all day. Elvis Presley, Buddy Holly . . . Oh, I was wondering if you'd like to go skating after work on Saturday?"

I nodded enthusiastically. Keysborough's ice rink had only opened a couple of months ago.

"Meet you at two o'clock? It's the earliest I can make it," Pat said.

*   *   *   *

When I finished at work at one o'clock on Saturday, I decided to walk down to the park and eat my sandwiches there. That would pass a bit of the time till I had to meet Pat.

The skies had been grey and it was chilly when I left Fine Print, but when I was about halfway to the park it started spluttering with rain. Drat. I'd left my umbrella at the shop.

I dashed back to Fine Print, hoping Mr Johnson hadn't already left. Fortunately the lights were still on.

Even though he'd put the *Closed* sign up, Mr Johnson had a customer.

"So sorry," I said as I entered. "I left my brolly in the kitchen."

Mr Johnson frowned and turned his attention to his customer, a lad of about eighteen, with dark hair and a black motorcycle jacket.

"And these belong to your gran, you say?"

"Yes, she's moving in with us. We don't have room for all her books."

I grabbed my brolly and hurried back outside.

Pat and I had a super time skating, and the afternoon went by all too quickly.

It was teeming down when we left the rink, and we sprinted to our bus stop under our brollies.

As the bus trundled down the high street, I spotted the lad in the motorcycle jacket sheltering in the shoe shop doorway.

He was smoking and chatting to another lad, one with blond hair and wearing a rust-coloured bomber jacket – the one who'd sold books to Mr Johnson during my first week.

I frowned. How strange that they knew each other. Or maybe not strange at all. Maybe the blond-haired one had recommended Mr Johnson as giving a fair price for books.

"Wasn't the ice rink smashing?" Pat said. "When shall we go again?"

I forgot about the lads as we worked out when we were next free.

*   *   *   *

"I've rather a lot of shelving for you today, Miss Russell," Mr Johnson said on Monday morning. "The dreadful weather this weekend meant I stayed inside and worked my way through the backlog of unsorted books."

Despite his words, I started when I saw the piles behind the counter. "Rather a lot of shelving" was an understatement.

He disappeared into the office while I began working my way through the piles. Romances, detective stories, science fiction, cookbooks . . .

And then, at the bottom of one pile, a collection of old girls' books, including some school stories.

I felt embarrassed about still enjoying this type of book at my age, so every time a customer entered the shop, I'd hurriedly put the book on the shelf and return to the counter.

One of the school stories was called "Pamela Of Peters'", and as I turned the pages, I spotted a reference to a character called Romola.

I grinned: she was just the plucky, popular kind of character I'd envisaged someone with that name having.

Now, where had I heard that name before?

Oh, yes, Dad had read it out – someone called Romola had been burgled a few weeks ago, and it had been in the newspaper.

I skim-read a few more pages of the book and was about to place it on the shelf when a thin piece of paper covered in writing slipped out of the book.

I read it, curious.

I found this book on the market the other day and discovered there's a character in it with the same name as you, Rommy! I remembered you collected books with your name in them. There can't be many books with your name in them, surely? Love, Erica.

I slid the note back in the book and filed it under "L" for the author, Edna Lake.

There couldn't be many real women called Romola, either, especially in Keysborough. Was the Romola who'd owned this book the same Romola who'd been burgled? Had she got rid of her books or had they been stolen?

The shop door jangled and I hurried back to the counter. A man about Mr Johnson's age, but with a full head of silver hair, was browsing the classical shelves.

"Can I help you with anything, sir?" I asked.

"No, thank you," he answered. "I'm just looking."

The acquisitions ledger lay on the counter, next to the sales book.

I opened it, found the pages for April, and ran my finger down the entries till I found the one I wanted.

Edna Lake, "Pamela Of Peters'", Thursday, April 17.

That had been my first Thursday at work.

The day the blond chap had come in early, selling a pile of books. A week after Romola Kendrick had been burgled.

I checked the entries for the other books purchased that day. One particular title caught my eye.

George Eliot, "Romola", Thursday, April 17.

"Is Mr Johnson in today?"

I jumped. The silver-haired man smiled at me from the other side of the counter.

I hurriedly closed the ledger.

"He's in the office. Can I help you?"

"I have some books I'm thinking of selling and I'm interested in what their value might be."

Soon Mr Johnson and the gentleman, who introduced himself as Malcolm Taylor, were discussing the collection.

"I've a first edition of 'Oliver Twist', and a signed copy of 'Jane Eyre'," Mr Taylor said.

I spotted the gleam in Mr Johnson's eyes, but he made a great show of flipping the pages of his appointment diary.

"Any night but tomorrow," Mr Taylor replied. "I'm visiting my elderly mother in the evening and I'll be staying overnight."

"Is Thursday afternoon convenient?" Mr Johnson asked. "That's when I usually do valuations, because it's early closing day."

"Yes, that sounds fine," Mr Taylor agreed.

Once he'd gone, I carried on shelving the remaining books. The final six were Chalet School books. I'd loved the Chalet School when I was younger.

The initials "BL" had been scrawled on the inside cover of all of them, and on the title pages had been written *To Barbara, love from Mother and Father*. They'd been presents for Christmas and her birthday.

Lucky Barbara. At her age I'd always been given clothes – and unfashionable ones at that.

*   *   *   *

Mum kept old newspapers in a big box in our box room, so we could use them for firelighters. That night, I sorted through them, searching for the April 17 issue of "The Keysborough Gazette".

When I found it, I turned to the police round-up.

And there she was: Miss Romola Kendrick, Hollies Road, Keysborough.

I bit my lip as I wondered if I should visit Romola, ask whether she'd got rid of her books or if they'd been stolen along with her jewellery.

The police round-up probably didn't list everything that was stolen – it would take up too much space.

It still bothered me that those two lads who'd brought in books knew each other. If they were selling stolen goods to Mr Johnson, they might get him into trouble.

I was about to go downstairs when it occurred to me that, if those two lads were robbers, they might have sold other stolen books to Fine Print.

I grabbed a pen and notebook and jotted down the names of people who'd been burgled over the past two months.

Excitement surged through me when I spotted the name *Barbara Leonard*. Could she be the owner of the Chalet School books that had been brought in?

I could hardly wait for the next morning so I could check when those books had been purchased.

*   *   *   *

"Miss Russell, could you look after the shop for a couple of hours after lunch?" Mr Johnson asked me next day. "There's a preview of an upcoming auction and I don't want to miss it."

"Of course," I agreed.

A week ago I'd have been pleased just to be left in charge of the shop. Now I was ecstatic at the unexpected opportunity to do some sleuthing.

As soon as he'd gone, I checked the acquisitions book.

The Chalet School books had been brought in a week after the burglary at Barbara Leonard's – just as had happened with Romola Kendrick's books.

Had the books the dark-haired boy brought in on Saturday afternoon come from another burglary? Those books were still in the office. Mr Johnson hadn't finished sorting through them yet.

My heart thumped and my mouth went dry as I turned the sign on the shop door to *Closed*.

Reassuring myself that it was in Mr Johnson's best interests to know if he was being duped by thieves, I twisted the handle of the office door.

It was locked.

He kept the key in a drawer under the sink. I grabbed it and unlocked the door.

Books covered every inch of shelf space in the office. I began opening books at random, looking for anything that indicated a match with any of the names in my notebook.

I found it: a pile of military memoirs, all inscribed *P. Maddocks*. Percy Maddocks had been burgled recently, according to last week's paper.

I put the books back down, wondering what to do next. Mr Johnson wasn't due back till just before five and it was only half-past two. Should I call the police or wait till I'd told Mr Johnson first?

Perhaps I should close the shop, head down to wherever the auction preview was and tell him. Then he could inform the police.

Mr Johnson's appointments diary lay on his desk, next to yet another pile of books.

I flipped through the pages, searching for today's date.

Tuesday June 3.

Auction preview 2.30 p.m., Newhampton Town Hall.

Evening: Taylor – 6 Carrs Lane, Keysborough.

Alarm bells sounded in my head at the second entry.

He wasn't visiting Mr Taylor tonight! Mr Taylor was going to be away overnight – he'd told us that.

I turned the page to Thursday, when they'd planned to meet.

Nothing.

Mind racing, I flipped back through the pages of the diary. I hoped I was wrong, and that Mr Johnson and Mr Taylor had simply rescheduled, but the diary confirmed that my suspicions were correct.

He'd had "appointments" with Romola Kendrick, Barbara Leonard, Percy Maddocks and Norman Edwards on the dates they'd been burgled!

Mr Johnson wasn't the victim in this – he was the villain!

No wonder he'd been irritated when I'd walked in unexpectedly when those lads were in the bookshop. They must have made up the "aunt" and "gran" excuses on the spot.

Mr Taylor lived near the railway station, only a 10-minute walk away.

I grabbed Mr Johnson's spare shop key from its drawer, shoved the diary and notebook in my handbag, and locked up the shop.

I had to warn Mr Taylor not to visit his mother tonight.

* * * *

"You worked this all out yourself?" Malcolm Taylor asked.

His eyes sparkled as we sat inside his living-room, together with his wife, who'd offered tea and cake.

He hadn't been surprised about being the target for a burglary. It turned out he was a private detective, employed by Romola Kendrick!

She'd become suspicious when a friend of hers was also burgled, with jewellery, money and some books being stolen. She thought the police weren't doing enough, so had hired a private detective instead.

"They'd both visited the bookshop and talked to him about books they collected," Mr Taylor told me. "So I interviewed some other people who'd been burgled – and some of them had visited the bookshop, too.

"I followed him to a jewellery store in Newhampton last week, which is owned by Mr Johnson's brother-in-law. Both of them were in on it and operated in the same way.

"Valuable jewellery and books were kept for a while, and then sold through catalogue or auction. Cheaper jewellery and books were kept for a few weeks then sold in the shops at a price that meant they were snapped up quickly.

"I was never leaving the house this evening. I'd already informed the police and we were setting a trap for him.

"But I'm very impressed with your sleuthing," Mr Taylor finished up. "And I hope you're just as good at acting.

"You need to go back to the bookshop and pretend everything's fine when Mr Johnson returns. We don't want him getting suspicious. Can you do that?"

"I think so," I replied.

I got back just in time to put the diary and the keys where I'd found them.

To my relief, Mr Johnson went straight back into the office, so I didn't have to make any awkward conversation.

"You what?" Mum asked when I got home and told her and Dad about the day's events. "Oh, Geri. What if you're wrong?"

"I'm not," I assured her. "Either way, though, I'll lose my job."

I felt glum about that. There were other bookshops, but I'd enjoyed working at Fine Print.

At around eight o'clock there was a knock at our door.

Dad let Mr Taylor in.

"The boys broke in as expected," he said. "The police were hidden in there and heard them talking about the money they'd get from Mr Johnson and his brother-in-law, so they were able to arrest them, too.

"We got your address from Mr Johnson, so we could tell you what happened. Mr Johnson will go to prison."

"I feel like I'm in a book," I remarked. "Solving a mystery like the girls in the books I used to read as a child."

I sighed.

"This doesn't end happily for me, though, because now I don't have a job."

"Yes, you do." Mr Taylor smiled. "I wasn't pretending to be a collector – I am one. I'm getting a bit long in the tooth to be a private detective and I've always fancied the idea of owning my own bookshop.

"So I'm going to buy one – and you, Miss Russell, will be my assistant. Assuming you're interested, of course?"

"Of course I am!" I exclaimed. "There's just one thing."

"What's that?"

"Could you please call me Geri?" ■

Grey Heron

ONE easily identifiable bird is the grey heron. While often spotted on UK shorelines and beside rivers, they will also take advantage of garden ponds if stocked with fish – so beware! These statuesque birds are from the same family as the stork, and as well as eating an abundance of fish, they will include crustaceans and small mammals such as voles in their diet.

Herons are predators which like to eat at dawn and dusk and prefer to hunt alone, but they nest together in colonies known as heronries.

They often return to the same nesting site in reedbeds or high up in trees, and rather than building a fresh nest, they just make repairs to old ones. The herons' eggs are pale blue, and they usually lay up to 10, with both parents feeding the young.

These long-necked, long-legged creatures have a black stripe from their eyes to the back of the head, and they are greyish-white, with black flight feathers. Both males and females look similar. They have an impressive wingspan of around six feet, so when they are in flight, they can be mistaken for a bird of prey. ■

Lead
The Way

by Jane Ayres

DO you have dogs of your own?" the friendly, tattooed receptionist, whose name badge read *Volunteer Eda,* asked. I shook my head.

"We were never allowed pets when I was a child. Mum hated the idea of animal hair all over the furniture, and Len – my late husband – was allergic."

I hoped she wouldn't see how anxious I felt about this.

When I was twelve, I'd tried to overcome my fear of dogs by walking our neighbour's cheeky little Cairn terrier, Tyke, who often slipped his lead and had me chasing after him.

Tyke and I had become best friends, even at his naughtiest, and I considered myself cured of my fear.

But that was a very long time ago.

"Could I start with one of the smaller dogs?" I asked.

Eda seemed surprised.

"I'm afraid you don't get to choose. Most of our rescue animals are Staffies or German shepherds. The ones that get abandoned the most."

"Oh. I didn't realise."

"I understand," Eda said. "If you want to help the rescue centre, we always need volunteers to help with fund-raising and publicity."

"I've wanted to be one of your dog walkers for ages. I just didn't have the time before, due to family commitments," I explained. "But circumstances have changed."

"Well, Bertha is really gentle. She's one of our long-term residents."

Eda returned with a brindle Staffie who looked scarily strong.

"She's very sweet, and incredibly loyal," Eda reassured me, "despite the way she was treated in the past before she was abandoned."

"Oh," I said.

I immediately felt a kinship with Bertha.

"Dogs are so forgiving," Eda added, handing me the lead.

"If you turn right at the gate, the path takes you to a big field. That should give her a nice long walk."

As soon as Bertha realised where we were headed, she tugged at the lead like a husky pulling a sled, and I had visions of being dragged down the muddy track.

But after a while, she settled down, and we both enjoyed the crisp morning air.

It was blissfully quiet. Just us and the fields. I began to relax and I sensed Bertha did, too.

As the sky threatened to darken after a low rumble of thunder, my thoughts clouded over, too.

"How could they be so selfish, moving away so far?" I asked Bertha. "Am I really such a dragon?"

Bertha huffed and puffed as the ground sloped upwards, still tugging. I realised my arm was aching.

"I bet it was down to her. Bossy Becky. Probably talked Jake into it.

"Why did he have to marry someone like that? I loved doing the school runs for them, and babysitting, but now I'll hardly see my grandchildren.

The Drawer

I'm going to clear out "the drawer" today,
And put some old stuff in the bin;
I've struggled to open and close it for weeks,
And I just can't fit any more in!

There are keys, but to what, I've forgotten,
Yet still I might need them one day;
And photos, not up to an album or frame,
But I don't want to throw them away.

There's a tooth in a tin, but that three-year-old grin
Now belongs to a thirty-year-old;
There's invites to weddings and parties long-gone—
But the memories they prompt are pure gold!

There are cards, in such careful handwriting;
"To Mummy," and later, "To Gran,"
With a tear in the eye, I put them aside:
Oh, dear. It's not going to plan.

But of course! There's another solution.
I pick up my phone with a grin;
And order a new chest of three lovely drawers—
With space for more treasures within!

Chris Young.

"Leeds is miles away. Too far to drive, especially with busy roads.

"It's all very well for Becky to say it's under three hours on the train from King's Cross, but then I have to get to London from Faversham, so it's half a day, really."

I'd felt quite lonely these past few weeks, unable to forgive my son and daughter-in-law for abandoning me so soon after I'd lost Len.

That was how it seemed, anyway.

But as I told Bertha all the things I'd bottled up, I started to wonder if feeling so hurt was distorting my version of events.

Deep down, I knew Jake and Becky were loving parents who only wanted the best for their children.

Like me and my Len.

"I just miss him so much, Bertha, especially not having him to talk to.

"But you have to get on with things, that's how I was brought up."

I sighed, looking again at the card in my hand.

"At least I got an invitation to the new baby's christening."

But then I frowned and shook my head.

"Of course, I won't be going. Not after the way Becky spoke to me on the phone last night."

"Although . . . to be fair, I suppose I was quite sharp with her."

Perhaps Becky and I were too much alike. Len had always joked about how bossy I could be.

As we left the field and passed the church, I realised I was now the one panting.

"I'm a bit out of condition, Bertha. Let's have a rest on this bench."

Bertha gazed up at me, her eyes gentle and soulful, and she sat meekly at my feet as I caught my breath.

"I need more regular exercise," I mumbled.

"But I'm enjoying this so far. Are you?"

Bertha looked back at me with those big, soulful eyes.

Wishing I'd remembered to bring my fleecy gloves, I thrust my hands into my parka coat pockets for warmth.

My fingers found the folded note that had been enclosed with the christening invite. I had been carrying it around with me.

I'd read it so many times since it arrived a fortnight ago that I almost knew the words off by heart, but I decided to share it with Bertha.

"Listen to this," I said to her.

Dear Mum,

Your grandkids miss you. We miss you. The spare room is always made up and we would love you to come and stay. A day, a week, longer – up to you. Sorry you are still upset over the move.

I know it's the other side of the country, but I couldn't turn down the offer of such a good job with the salary to match. We can afford a lovely home in the country with a garden for the kids.

There's a great local school and Becky has picked up some regular freelance work, so things are turning out even better than we expected.

It would make us both so happy if you made it to the christening, and it would mean the world for the whole family to be together again. Please come. Love, Jake.

The wind must have caught my eyes, because they were watering.

I put the note away.

"Time to go back, Bertha," I said, getting to my feet.

Bertha followed my lead, walking enthusiastically by my side.

I couldn't help but smile.

Ten minutes later, the rescue centre was in sight, and Bertha slowed down markedly, clearly reluctant to return.

"How did it go?" Eda asked.

"The time flew by," I replied, glancing thoughtfully at the *Volunteers Wanted* poster on the wall.

"Although Bertha seems to have run out of steam now we're back."

"Poor thing, I keep hoping one day some kind soul will take to her. All she wants is a for ever home." Eda sighed.

Home. That's when I realised how lucky I was.

Bertha had truly been abandoned, whereas I still had a family who loved me and wanted me.

Had I left it too late?

"So, will you be back?" Eda asked.

"Not for a few days. I need to make a trip to Leeds, to build some bridges."

"Well, thanks for today. I'm sure Bertha appreciated it." I could tell from Eda's voice she didn't expect me to return.

She looked pleasantly surprised when I added, "But I'd definitely like to take Bertha out again and get to know her better. If that's OK?"

The Staffie's tail wagged tentatively and her ears pricked up.

I smiled as I made a fuss of her.

"Where else would I find such a good listener?" ∎

Bishop Auckland, Co. Durham

The ancient market town of Bishop Auckland is located in the Vale of Durham, where the River Wear and the River Gaunless join.

From its earliest incarnations this has been a desirable spot. Initially the town was presented to the Earl of Northumberland in AD 1000 for defending the church against the Scots. Twenty years later, King Cnut awarded it to the Bishop of Durham.

The bishops in the area enjoyed special status. Not only were they responsible for church affairs, but they governed the area between the Tyne and the Tees on behalf of the Crown.

According to legend, in the Middle Ages the whole valley was terrorised by a wild boar as big as a cow: the Pollard Brawn. As in all the best stories, it needed a big reward from the bishop and the derring-do of a crafty knight to save the day!

The influence of the powerful Prince-Bishops, as they became known, is evident in the town today, with the Bishop's Palace, or Auckland Castle, a popular tourist attraction. The castle was the country residence of the bishops for over 900 years and now sits within a 150-acre deer park.

Bouquets Of Love

by Alyson Hilbourne

HE knock at the door startled Jean.

"Who's that so early in the morning?" she muttered to herself. She put down the tea towel she was holding and hurried to answer it.

Standing on the doorstep was a young lad with gingery hair, tufts of a moustache growing over his top lip, and spots.

He thrust a bouquet of flowers into Jean's hands and hurried off.

"I – I . . . Thank you!" Jean called after him, somewhat flustered.

She stared at the arrangement in surprise and delight.

Who was sending her flowers out of the blue? Was it her son, Oscar, from California? Or her daughter, Juliet, in Devon?

Charlie had never bought her flowers even when they were courting.

He hadn't had a romantic bone in his body, and she'd wondered again and again over the years what the bright young thing that became her replacement had seen in him.

She shut the door and took the flowers through to the kitchen.

She was about to unwrap the Cellophane when the florist's card fell out on to the tabletop: *Collins, 24 Mill Lane.*

Jean sighed. The flowers weren't for her at all.

She lived at number 24 Mill Road. The delivery boy had made a mistake.

For a fleeting moment Jean thought about keeping the bouquet — it was a pretty pink selection of roses, alstroemerias and lilies — but she was too honest.

She picked up the florist's card and delved in her bag to find her phone.

"Good morning," she said when the call was answered. "A lad has just delivered a bouquet of flowers but I don't think they are for me. The address on the card is Mill Lane and I live on Mill Road."

"Oh, not again!"

Jean could hear the frustration in the voice on the phone.

"He really is useless. I'm so sorry, and thank you for ringing. I'll send him to pick them up."

Jean put the phone down, smiled at the flowers and carried on with the washing-up.

A few hours later she'd done half an hour's weeding in the garden and made a cake when she noticed the bouquet was still in the hall by the door.

"Tsk," she said. "Someone will be waiting for those."

She rang the florist again.

"Sorry. We are so busy. We have a wedding tomorrow, with a nightmare mother demanding all sorts of changes, so we're rushed off our feet getting the church flowers and bouquets ready. I'll send him over now."

Jean made herself a cup of tea and sat down to drink it, but she kept glancing at the flowers.

The smell from the lilies had filled the house.

Mill Lane was not far, she reasoned. She could drop them round there herself.

Jean rang the florist's to let them know.

She took her cup to the kitchen, collected her handbag, pulled on a light jacket and set off carrying the flowers.

Mill Lane was a street of terraced cottages, each with a little yard and short path up to the front door.

Jean rang the bell at number 24.

For a moment she thought no-one was at home, but then the door was yanked open and a man with silvery hair and glasses perched on his head appeared on the step.

"Those were meant to come this morning!" he said, grabbing the bouquet from Jean's hands.

"They –" Jean began, but before she could say anything more the door was slammed in her face and she was left blinking on the doorstep.

Jean gave a bark of laughter and stepped back. Her legs were shaking and her heart racing.

She hadn't even been given a chance to explain. Did she look like a delivery boy?

Some people were so rude. Jean almost wished she'd kept the flowers.

The man didn't deserve them. She hoped he didn't have some poor wife in there. No doubt she lived a desperate life.

Jean hurried home and tried not to think about the encounter. It had made her feel a little queasy.

* * * *

By Monday morning she had put all thoughts of flowers from her mind and was busy changing the sheets on her bed when the doorbell rang.

The first thing she saw as she opened the door was a small bunch of carnations and baby's breath.

She blinked.

"I've come to apologise."

Jean looked up from the flowers and saw the grey-haired man from Mill Lane.

"I'm sorry. The florist rang me to apologise. They told me about the mix-up of addresses and explained that you had brought the flowers round. I was rude and out of order.

"I hope these make up for it in some way." He thrust the flowers at Jean. "All I can say is that I'd asked for my flowers in the morning, and it made me cross they were so late."

"Thank you," Jean said stiffly. She thought for a moment the man looked rather lost, but then she remembered how rude he'd been, and felt glad she wasn't the florist. "That's kind of you."

The man gave a quick nod and turned away.

Jean watched him leave as she stood on the step holding her flowers. Then she took them inside and arranged them in a vase.

It was the following day when she was taking a short cut through the cemetery to the high street that Jean spotted the same man, crouched down in front of a gravestone.

He was pulling the roses out of the same bunch of flowers that had been delivered to her.

The roses were already wilting, the buds dangling over the stems.

They probably didn't get in water quickly enough, Jean thought. That's a shame.

She stopped and watched for a moment, and was about to walk on when the man looked up. He did a double take.

"Hello again," he said, a look of contrition on his face. "I'm sorry again for my rudeness. The flowers were for the anniversary of my wife's death. I was cross when they didn't arrive."

He waved at the gravestone, which was still clear and easy to read.

She felt herself softening.

"That's nice," she said. "How long were you married?"

"Thirty-five years," the man said quietly, looking at the headstone. "Not long enough. I still miss her."

"I'm sure she appreciates the flowers," Jean said, feeling it was a silly thing to say.

The man stood up and gave her a quick smile. Then he bent down and picked up the roses he'd removed.

"The roses always die first, but Clare did love them.

"Anyway, that's the anniversary dealt with for another year. I'll go and collect the flowers myself next year, I think, rather than rely on their delivery service."

"Don't be too hard on them," Jean told him. "I believe they were very busy with a wedding and a nightmare mother of the bride."

The man gave a mock shiver and Jean laughed.

"I suppose you think I'm a bit daft, being so insistent on getting the flowers here early, but Clare preferred flowers to anything," he explained. "She'd rather have fresh flowers than go out to dinner or have chocolates.

"We only had a tiny garden, but she filled it with tubs and pots of flowers. I'm afraid I've rather let it go. I don't have the enthusiasm."

"I don't think that's daft," Jean replied. "It sounds lovely to me. My husband never thought to buy me flowers."

She pulled a face.

"It was so thoughtful of you to bring those carnations yesterday."

"Actually . . ." The man shuffled his feet. "I should be honest. The florist was going to bring you those flowers by way of compensation for your time and disturbance. I said I'd deliver them. I felt it was the least I could do."

"What?" Jean said, stepping back. "And I thought you'd bought them for me!"

The man shrugged.

"Sorry. I was about to explain to you but you looked pretty cross, so I scarpered."

Jean narrowed her eyes.

"I was cross because you were so rude at first," she told him.

"Guilty as charged." The man looked down at his feet. "Look, we seem to have got the wrong idea of each other.

"If you're not busy, could I buy you a coffee or tea as a real thank-you?"

Jean thought for a moment. She wasn't busy. She hadn't been busy since the kids had left home.

There was always plenty to do, but she wasn't busy.

The man gathered his rubbish and together they made their way out of the cemetery.

"Henry," the silver-haired man said.

"Jean," she replied.

"Have you lived here all your life?" Henry asked.

"Yes, although not always in Mill Road," Jean explained.

"How about here?" Henry stopped at a small tea room with two small tables outside and a pleasant smell of toast coming from the open door.

"Oh, yes. I've been here before." Jean smiled.

Henry pretended to mop his brow.

"Phew! Something we agree on," he said with a twinkle in his eye.

*   *   *   *

Two years later, Jean and Henry walked together into the florist.

"I'd like to order a bouquet," Jean declared. "For my wedding. Something simple."

"Do I know you?" the florist asked with her head on one side.

"You should," Henry replied. "I have several orders with you. An annual bouquet for my late wife's grave and a regular order for my soon-to-be bride."

Henry beamed at Jean and she grinned back.

"Of course! I remember now!" The florist smacked her forehead in mock anguish. "The bouquet mix-up. Mill Lane and Mill Road."

"That's it." Jean nodded.

"I hope we've got it right now," the florist said.

"It's fine," Jean assured her. "Although it won't matter soon as we'll be moving to a new address.

"But I suppose we owe you some thanks," she continued. "Two years ago, your mix-up kick-started our relationship."

She smiled at Henry.

"That's wonderful!" the florist exclaimed, clapping her hands together. "So romantic.

"Now, have a look at these photographs and tell me if you see something you fancy. We can change the flowers or foliage to suit."

She passed Jean a binder of photographs.

At they were leaving the shop, bouquet chosen and paid for, Jean turned to Henry.

"You won't cancel the flowers once we're married?" she asked with a frown.

He had wooed her for the last two years with a weekly bouquet of flowers.

"Fresh flowers each week, Mum?" Juliet had asked her. "He's a keeper."

Jean thought so, too, because when Henry asked for her hand she'd accepted.

But she still wanted her flowers.

"Not as long as they're delivered correctly," Henry replied, smiling at her. ■

Blackbird

Shutterstock.

YOU can't beat a dawn chorus on a spring morning. And, while the blackbird may be less colourful than many of its feathered friends, it makes up for this with melodious song. The male of the species has a bright golden-yellow beak and the eye is also rimmed in a similar hue.

The female is brown with lighter brown flecks on the breast and is usually smaller than the male.

With between three and five blue-green eggs in each clutch, nesting begins around March and the nests are usually low down.

Blackbirds will often come back to raise their young in the same location and, once the young hatch, both parents feed them. The breeding pair usually stays together for life.

The blackbird is commonly found in our gardens and some can be very tame, especially if there's food on offer – their diet consists of a variety of insects, spiders, worms and berries. ■

The Write Stuff

by Sharon Haston

W**HAT** are you writing?"

Sighing, I slammed my notebook shut. My sister Bethany is always poking her nose into my business.

At fifteen, she's only two years older than me, but you wouldn't think it from the way she tries to boss me around.

"Nothing," I replied.

I didn't tell her I was entering a writing competition in case I didn't win.

Bethany's always winning at her dancing competitions, Mum has lots of bowling trophies, and Dad is the top player at his golf club.

I started ballet lessons when I was younger, but I was always facing the wrong way and bumping into everyone. I'm even worse at sport.

I'll never live down the embarrassment of having to be rescued from the top of the pommel horse by my best friend Sophie.

But I do love English at school, especially writing stories. Miss Mackinnon's my favourite teacher and she suggested I enter this competition.

I felt a warm glow when she said she thought my stories were excellent.

"Is it your secret diary?" Bethany tried to grab my notebook, but I batted her hand away. "I bet there's someone you fancy at school and you're writing about him. What's his name?"

I rolled my eyes. If I didn't tell her something, she'd keep going on about it and try to sneak a peek.

"If you must know, it's my writer's notebook," I said loftily.

She looked nonplussed.

"What are you talking about?"

"Miss Mackinnon said I should start writing for my own pleasure, and writers always carry a notebook with them in case an idea comes up."

Bethany yawned, opening the fridge.

"How boring. I can't imagine doing schoolwork at home if I didn't have

Illustration by Ruth Blair.

to. A secret diary would have been more exciting."

Mum arrived, loaded with shopping bags.

"Who's keeping a secret diary?"

"Nobody. I'm keeping a notebook as I want to be a writer," I said, exasperated.

Bethany snorted.

"Now she thinks she's going to be the next Agatha Christie."

"Our Maisie maybe will be a famous writer. All her teachers praise her compositions." Mum gallantly leapt to my defence.

"Miss Mackinnon says I should write about what I know, so you better watch out," I told Bethany darkly, thinking Mum would be very interested in knowing she put on more make-up on the school bus.

Bethany took a yoghurt from the fridge and bounded upstairs.

"I don't want to be in your stupid story!" she yelled.

"Ignore her," Mum said. "Keep going with your story. But I'm not sure about writing about what you know. Wouldn't it be better if you wrote about something exciting? Maybe a fantasy with dragons or princesses?"

I forced a smile. "Game Of Thrones" is Mum's favourite programme. I'm too young to watch it, but I don't care because I don't fancy it at

all. I like a mystery story where I can guess the ending.

"Be careful what you write in it, Maisie, in case it falls into the wrong hands," Sophie warned me the next day when I told her about entering the competition and my notebook.

"I'd be mortified if Oliver Jones found out I fancy him, and I never want Mr Forsyth to find out it was me who scorched the desk with the Bunsen burner," she added. "It was an accident."

I looked out the bus window. My friends and family seemed to think I'd be writing about them.

As if! School science lessons were far too dull to write about.

And Oliver Jones, with his constant sneery expression, wasn't my idea of handsome.

*　*　*　*

I wasn't afraid of telling Gran about the competition.

I could trust her not to tell the rest of my family. She never gave away any of my secrets.

"You go for it, Maisie. Remember the stories we used to make up when you stayed over? You always had a great imagination."

I smiled, remembering how we'd turned Gran's garden into a jungle full of tigers and elephants; her sofa became a ship where we met

Afternoon Tea

There's Granny's rosebud cake stand set upon the cloth of white,
Piled high with almond slices and sweet fairy cakes so light.
Tiny sausage rolls and golden scones with strawberry jam,
Some dainty finger sandwiches of egg or cheese and ham.
Macaroons and vol au vents, a homemade quiche Lorraine,
And finally a fruitcake we can cut and come again.
With a steaming pot of loose-leaf tea, the tasty spread's complete,
Now all the family gathers round for a well-earned Sunday treat.

Laura Tapper.

pirates, and her stairs the portal into a world of fairies and elves.

"Have you heard Maisie's keeping a notebook, Gran?" Bethany said when she arrived after school. "She's going to put us all in her stories."

She glared at me.

"Maisie won't put us in her story, will you, love?" Gran poured our tea. "We're all too boring and ordinary. Nobody wants to read about me making jam and hoeing the garden."

Gran's rhubarb jam, which I spread on my scone, tasted great, and her garden was gorgeous, but I wasn't going to write about them.

The theme of the competition was magic, so I couldn't write about everyday stuff.

When I told Sophie that, she put her hand to her mouth.

"Don't write about the time we gathered dandelions and daisies to make a spell for rain on our school sports day."

I laughed at the memory. Sophie hates sport as much as me.

Our spell didn't work. It was a sunny day, so we had to endure coming last in all the races. I was hardly going to write about that.

*   *   *   *

I stared at my phone, reading the e-mail 20 times before finally believing it.

"I won!" I jumped up from the sofa and danced around the living-room.

"Won what? Is it a holiday to Florida?" Bethany looked up from her own phone.

"No, it's the writing competition. I've actually won it."

Mum and Bethany stared at me.

"What competition?" Mum asked.

I'd forgotten I hadn't told them.

"That's amazing. Well done!" Mum hugged me when I explained.

"Well done, sis." Bethany nudged me. "What is the prize, though? Is it a holiday?"

"A book token." I smiled.

Bethany looked bewildered.

"You wrote stuff in your own time, when you didn't have to, for a book token!"

I laughed. I'd never seen her read a book outside of school.

When she wasn't winning dance competitions, she went cycling, or swimming in ponds.

She was what Mum called "outdoorsy".

The thought of swimming amongst frogs and fish filled me with horror.

"That's a great prize for you, Maisie." Mum frowned at Bethany.

"Can we read your story?" Bethany asked, to my amazement.

I didn't think she'd be interested. Maybe she was still worried I'd revealed all her secrets.

I held my breath as she read, worried about her response. I couldn't bear it if she made fun of it.

"I'm in it. Eleanor is me!" she said once she'd finished.

"What are you talking about?"

"It's obvious. Eleanor is the older, wiser sister. I'm glad you appreciate me."

She gave me a rare hug before running off, presumably to tell all her friends she was in my story.

*   *   *   *

"It's a wonderful story, Maisie. I feel honoured to be in it." Gran wiped away a tear and squeezed my hand.

I was confused.

"Which character is you?"

"Zelena, of course. The wise woman who's secretly a witch, stirring up potions to make the world a better place."

My eyes were as wide as the saucer that was holding Gran's best china teacup.

She must be joking. My thoroughly modern gran with her blonde bobbed hair, jeans and huge smile couldn't look less like a witch if she tried.

I thought of the TV show "Sabrina" and shrugged.

Witches did come in all shapes and sizes, I supposed.

The one in my story wasn't exactly like the green one with the pointy hat in "The Wizard Of Oz".

* * * *

"Congratulations, Maisie, I knew you'd win," Sophie said as we waited for the bus. "I also knew you'd put me in it."

Not another one!

"Which character are you?" I asked wearily.

"The wise-cracking best friend who comes up with all the fab, wacky suggestions, of course. Who else could it be?"

I put on my sunglasses to try to hide my expression.

What was Sophie talking about? I was the one who was funny and came up with all the great ideas!

* * * *

At home, I wrote in my secret diary.

I did actually have one, but it was well hidden and had a lock. Bethany would never find it.

I couldn't believe they thought they were in my story. They'd been so adamant I wasn't to write about them, but now they thought they were in it they were all chuffed to bits. It was really weird.

I gnawed my pen, thinking about my story.

From my window, I saw Bethany stroll into the garden, licking a lolly.

Maybe she had a point about being the older wiser sister, even though I would never admit it to her.

She did take me to the cinema to cheer me up after I found out my school trip to Paris was cancelled.

She also taught me how to do my eyeliner so I didn't look like one of the pandas we saw at Edinburgh Zoo.

Sophie was a great best friend who did make me giggle, even in boring Maths classes.

And she had suggested roller-skating, which was great fun.

But Gran as a witch?

I thought about my lovely, caring gran.

Well, she did make a lot of unusual recipes that always turned out to taste amazing. Dad called them her "concoctions", as he said the ingredients shouldn't really belong together.

She did make the world a better place by helping out at the food bank and volunteering in our local charity shop.

Miss Mackinnon did say "write about what you know", and maybe I did without realising it.

I slipped my writer's notebook into my shorts before heading out into the sunshine.

At last, I didn't feel as if I was the only one around here who never won anything. I could hold my head up high.

Yesterday, Miss Mackinnon, who was delighted for me, pointed out another writing competition I could enter.

It's called "My Family". I don't think I'll tell them just yet! ■

Beside The Seaside

by Sarah Swatridge

M Y goodness, Enid, you are chipper this morning," his lordship said. He was reading his newspaper in the library while Enid was clearing the grate.

"Shall I come back later, sir?" she asked.

"No, that's not necessary. You carry on!" He seemed somewhat flustered. "But please refrain from singing."

"Sorry, sir. I had no idea I was doing it." Enid gave a little curtsey and returned to her chores.

After only a few minutes, he folded his newspaper, sat back and crossed his legs.

"Come here, Enid," he said.

Enid stood, brushed down her apron and presented herself.

The master studied her for a moment or two, then smiled.

"What's got into you?" he asked. "You seem full of the joys of spring. Have you met a young man?"

"Oh, no, sir." Enid was shocked by his suggestion.

"What's put you in such a good mood, then?"

Enid looked down at her second-hand boots.

"Come on. I want to know, because I've been in Italy for a month, which was supposed to cheer me up, but it didn't do the trick."

"I'm sorry, sir. Didn't you have a good holiday?"

"It took simply ages to get there, and when we arrived the place was hot and dusty. The food tasted odd. Even the water didn't agree with her ladyship."

"No-one spoke a word of English, and by the time the newspapers arrived, they were at least a day late."

"Sorry to hear that, sir."

"I seem to remember you had a week with your aunt; was that a better experience?"

"Oh, I had a wonderful time, sir."

Set in 1920

Illustration by Shutterstock.

"Wonderful? How?" he asked her. "What was so good about it?"

"It felt so good to breathe in the sea air. I ate fresh fish every day, sat on a donkey, and borrowed my cousin's bathing suit and went in the sea.

"It was freezing, but I felt alive! If you know what I mean, sir?"

"Now I suppose you'd like to go and live by the seaside?"

"Oh, no, sir," Enid was quick to tell him. "Truly, I had the best time, but it was even better to come home."

"I, too, was glad to get home," his lordship agreed.

"I better get on, sir, or Mrs Winter will have my guts for garters!"

Enid hurriedly finished clearing the grate, and made up the fire ready to be lit.

* * * *

Lord Henley stood and stared out of the large bay window into the distance.

Nothing had been quite the same since the Great War, and now they had the Spanish flu to contend with.

No wonder it was harder to recruit, and then to keep staff, both inside the manor and on the estate.

"Is everything all right?" Lady Henley asked as she entered the room. "You look as though you've the world on your shoulders."

"I want to expand the farm, to try new crops and rear more cattle, but we've barely enough workers to manage what we have now."

"It's the same for me," Lady Henley told him. "Daisy has been acting

61

as lady's maid but, quite frankly, she's much more suited to the scullery. "Servants are so hard to come by." She sighed. "It was different before the war. We had people queuing up for work and they were all so loyal!"

* * * *

Downstairs, Enid was set to polish the footwear that the family had brought back from their month in Europe.

"I've never seen so many pairs of shoes. I only have these boots, and those are hand-me-downs."

Mr Reed was busy polishing the master's riding boots.

Enid told him of her strange conversation with his lordship.

"I don't know why they bothered to go," the footman said. "From what I hear, they wanted Cook to do the same meals she prepares here, which was difficult, because it was hard to get some of the ingredients.

"They didn't leave the house they were staying in because it was too hot outside. They didn't entertain any guests. Her ladyship worked on her tapestry and his lordship read old newspapers and complained about insects and the unsavoury smells."

"His lordship didn't seem to enjoy himself," Enid admitted. "I felt awful bad telling him what a wonderful time I'd had."

Mr Reed raised an eyebrow.

"He asked me about my holiday!" Enid added defensively.

* * * *

Empire Day was fast approaching on May 24, and Lady Henley had been considering if she ought to give the servants a half day.

"The trouble is," she confessed to Lord Henley, "I don't know what we would do without them."

Lord Henley carefully folded his newspaper and looked at his wife.

"I have an idea," he said. "I read an article about a company who were losing workers to a competitor, so they arranged a day out for employees.

"It was a great success, and they've made it an annual event. Needless to say, they've not only retained their staff, but morale has increased."

"I don't really see the connection," Lady Henley replied.

"I suggest we hire a charabanc and take the entire household to the seaside for the day. I think the fresh sea air would do us all some good."

At that point, Enid came in with their tray of tea.

"You recently stayed with your aunt on the coast?" he asked her.

Enid nodded.

"Can you tell her ladyship and me what you enjoyed most?"

"The taste of the fish and chips, the sea breeze in my hair, the feel of the sand between my toes; hearing the sound of the gulls, the —"

"Thank you, Enid." Her ladyship cut her off. "I can tell you had the most wonderful time."

"I did, your ladyship. I love visiting my aunt, but it's nice to come home."

Lord Henley waited until Enid had left the room before addressing his wife.

"Did you see the way her face lit up? I've never seen her so animated."

"Indeed," her ladyship conceded. "But can we trust them to come back?"

"We shall accompany them. I've heard of a very pleasant hotel where one can take tea and have a good view of the pleasure beach, without actually having to venture down to the water."

"It's good to hear you enthuse about something," Lady Henley told him. "You've been so melancholy lately."

∗ ∗ ∗ ∗

Almost as soon as the day trip was announced, Lord Henley became aware of the change of atmosphere in the manor.

Lady Henley was careful to show more of an interest in the menu Cook had suggested for the servants' picnic, and confided in him that Daisy, her usually dour lady's maid, had been caught smiling!

The sun shone as the charabanc pulled up outside the manor house.

Lord Henley watched from the drawing-room window; he hardly recognised some of them, dressed in their Sunday best.

In order to allow their chauffeur to join in the festivities, he'd offered to drive Lady Henley and himself in his new motor car. He was looking forward to getting behind the wheel more than breathing sea air.

Lord Henley thoroughly enjoyed the sense of freedom he got from driving himself on a beautiful sunny day.

He was thankful his wife entered into the spirit of things, and had bought a new outfit especially for the occasion.

It had been arranged she should meet with her sister and their niece at the Grand Hotel. Lord Henley gave them the opportunity to talk while he took himself for a walk, promising to return for luncheon.

Lord Henley strolled along the front, past a very ornate shelter.

He could hear the gulls Enid had spoken of, but he also heard music. A band was playing.

This was a world of colour, so unlike the wood-panelled library where he spent the majority of his time.

He spotted Enid. She was standing on the sand with her boots in one hand.

She seemed mesmerised by a children's puppet show. One puppet, dressed in red and yellow, was intent on hitting another.

Lord Henley paused at a stall selling bright pink seaside rock. He bought four sticks: one each for his wife, his sister-in-law, his niece and himself.

As he left, he realised he would never have entered the tobacconist's in the village to buy confectionery, but here, just for the day, it felt different.

He saw Enid looking at straw hats.

"It wouldn't suit you," he said, making her jump. "Are you enjoying your day?"

"I most certainly am, sir," Enid replied, giving a little curtsey.

"You realise this is all down to you?"

"Me, sir?"

"Yes. If you hadn't been so cheerful after your holiday, I would never have considered this outing."

Enid looked down at her bare feet. She was still carrying her boots. They strolled along the promenade.

"May I treat you to an ice-cream, as a thank-you?" Lord Henley asked.

"I shouldn't, sir," Enid said. "Cook's prepared a marvellous picnic."

"I, too, have luncheon to return to," he confessed. "But they do look tempting."

He smiled at Enid, and she grinned when Lord Henley approached the ice-cream seller.

"It'll have to be our secret," he told her as he handed Enid a little pot of the cold dessert.

"Delicious," Enid said as she licked the creamy white ice-cream.

His lordship agreed, although he knew his wife would be horrified to know he was eating something on the street!

"Now run along, Enid, and enjoy the picnic," he said, dismissing her.

He watched her carrying her boots by their laces, and thought about how you could do things beside the seaside that you would never entertain doing whilst at home.

Things like going barefoot or eating a dessert on the pavement!

He smiled, enjoying his liberty.

As much as Lord Henley had enjoyed venturing along the promenade, he was pleased to be back in the Grand Hotel with his wife and her family.

They were politely grateful for the stick of seaside rock.

"If nothing else, it will serve as a reminder of today." He laughed. "You don't really have to try it."

After luncheon, Lord Henley was surprised to hear his wife request a short stroll around the hotel gardens so she could breathe in the sea air, hear the gulls and understand what all the fuss was about.

"I think I'll join you," he said, and offered her his arm.

"These gardens are delightful," Lady Henley said as she admired several of the plants and small trees she'd never seen before. "Would a seaside garden work at home?"

✳   ✳   ✳   ✳

All too soon, it was time to head back to the comfort of the manor.

Lord Henley's motor car followed the charabanc for part of the journey. They could hear their servants singing and congratulated themselves on a successful day.

"I'd say that was quite a triumph," Lord Henley declared.

"I, too, admit to feeling invigorated by the sea air," Lady Henley agreed. "It's a shame we no longer have a team of gardeners.

"I cannot see Timpson having the time to make me a seaside garden."

"In that case, we'll have to make an annual pilgrimage to the coast, so you can breathe the sea air and wander amongst the palm trees."

"That would be delightful, and I am sure it will boost our servants' morale. From now on, this is how we'll celebrate Empire Day – with a jolly day by the seaside." ∎

St John's Town Of Dalry, Dumfries And Galloway

Pilgrimages were all the rage in the Middle Ages. From Canterbury to the Camino de Santiago and beyond, wherever there was a holy relic, there were visitors seeking blessings.

The best part was that there were so many holy sites, you could probably manage a pilgrimage not too far from home.

For Scottish pilgrims, that might mean a trek from Edinburgh or Glasgow to the first recorded Christian church in the country.

That was the church of St Ninian, built at the end of the fourth century in Whithorn in Galloway.

Although it didn't require a voyage overseas, it was still a long journey, and travellers needed somewhere to rest along the way.

Step in the Knights Hospitaller of the Order of St John of Jerusalem. The Knights owned land in the Galloway Hills on the route from Edinburgh and established St John's Town of Dalry as a stopping place for the pilgrims.

Later, the village became notable as the centre of the 1666 Pentland Rising, a revolt by Covenanter dissidents against the Scottish government of the time. The revolt was put down and the Dalry Covenanters punished harshly for their part in it.

The Burning Bush memorial sculpture, installed in the village in 2004, is testament to their memory.

Stitched Up!

— by Laura Tapper —

W**HAT** do I know about modern nine-year-olds, Yvonne? It would be bad enough one to one, but in a room of thirty, I wouldn't have a clue."

Erica looked around for the pot of jam on the café table. The two old friends met up once a fortnight for a walk in their local National Trust gardens and to indulge in a leisurely coffee.

"You said last week that you've been missing your grandchildren and were looking to do some volunteering, so when the appeal went out, I thought of you straight away."

Erica plopped two misshapen brown sugar lumps into her cappuccino.

It was true, she found the tail end of her week dragged now that her son, David, and his young family had moved more than 80 miles away.

As soon as her first granddaughter had been born, Erica had been pleased to reduce her hours as a dental hygienist to form part of the childcare package which enabled her daughter-in-law to return to work.

Eighteen months later, a second pregnancy gave her a pigeon pair to look after and Erica had loved the balance of her week.

Most people assumed that, relieved of granny-duties, she would be keen to go back into the workplace full time, but she was on the lookout for something new and different.

"When I said that, I was thinking of something quiet, cultured and civilised – like assisting in the gardens here, or maybe becoming one of the guides in the main house – not entering the lion's den of primary education!" Erica's brow wrinkled in distress at the idea.

"I mean, I've coped well enough with Effie and Alfie, but what you're suggesting would be a world away from that. And I wasn't much good at fractions or spellings back in the day, so I don't suppose I've improved!" Yvonne laughed.

"Look, they only want someone to come in and lend a hand for this one project and you have all the skills you need for that.

"It'll have to be done in small groups, anyway, and I'll be there to make sure you don't get landed with anything you can't handle."

* * * *

"Watch again and copy what I do." Erica looked down and smiled at the concentration on the young face beside her. "Slide the needle in at

Illustration by Helen Welsh.

the back, wind the wool around, and then pull the point through here."

"Oh! What did I do wrong?" The words came with a growl of frustration.

Resting her own work in her lap, Erica held out her hands for her companion's knitting.

"Don't worry – I can soon put that right. You just need to hold the wool a bit tighter."

At that moment, Miss Sullivan called for the class's attention and Erica immediately looked over to the teacher, who was standing in front of windows criss-crossed with masking tape, holding up a painted silhouette of an aeroplane.

"Joel's done a marvellous job with this one, so who can tell me which plane this is?"

The room fell quiet while the children considered and then a couple of tentative hands went up.

Erica quickly corrected Metiya's error and then settled in to get a couple of rows done to help the girl progress a bit further, keeping her eyes on the teacher all the time.

"OK, if we were out playing and spotted this flying overhead, we'd have to decide if it was British or German, to know whether to raise the alarm or not, so hands up for British," Miss Sullivan said, altering the task to encourage more of the children to join in.

A few more hands went up, but before there was a chance to hear any answers, they were interrupted by a loud wailing sound which prompted an immediate response from the class, who all dived under their tables with their arms over their heads.

The lights went out and Yvonne, who was the class teaching assistant, whispered discreetly in Erica's ear that she didn't need to take part in this element of the activities if she didn't want to.

However, throwing herself into the spirit of the re-enactment day, she popped her knitting in her wicker basket and tucked herself under the wooden desk near where she'd been sitting, taking Metiya with her.

Once there, Erica could feel that the nine-year-old was shaking, her hands clamped tightly over her ears and her eyes squeezed shut.

The siren stopped and there followed a soundtrack of bomb explosions, presumably to give the children a sense of what life in wartime might have been like.

Still Metiya shivered, rocking herself gently back and forth.

Erica didn't know what to do and tried to catch Miss Sullivan's eye, but she was busy with another child who felt sick.

Yvonne had also disappeared and Erica didn't want to abandon the child to go in search of her, so she decided the best thing was to stay where she was and rested a reassuring hand on the girl's back until the all-clear sounded.

As soon as the "air raid" was over, the classroom itself exploded with excitable chatter and the staff allowed the children a few minutes to collectively process what they'd just experienced.

In contrast, Metiya returned quietly to her seat and picked up her knitting, her long, dark hair shielding her face from view as she focused on the task in hand.

Erica joined her.

"I can remember my grandma telling me about how they took their knitting down into the shelters with them to pass the time. She was the one who taught me how to knit when I was a little girl," Erica said.

Metiya glanced up briefly through her curtain of hair.

"I made a scarf for my teddy and I dropped more stitches than I knitted, if I remember rightly." Erica chuckled quietly.

After a pause her tone became more serious.

"It was frightening for my mum during the air raids, though – especially at night time, when they were all crowded in the shelters. She was only about five when war broke out."

Metiya carried on winding the yarn around the needles and gripping them tightly as she tried her hardest to keep hold of all her stitches this time.

"When I was six, there was a fire." The girl's voice wasn't much more than a whisper and Erica had to lean in slightly to catch her words. "Me and my sister were asleep. The smoke alarm woke us up. It was so loud."

Over the next 15 minutes, Erica sat quietly knitting and listening, while Metiya haltingly told the tale of what had happened to her: how the fire brigade had rescued her family, but their home had been destroyed, forcing them to live with her grandparents.

How they had only recently been able to move into their own new home at last; how she'd just started at that school a few weeks ago; how sirens still frightened her.

"Well, I think you are a very brave young lady and Miss Sullivan is lucky to have you in her class."

Metiya looked up, her face brightening slightly.

"And I must say, you're doing a wonderful job on your knitting now," Erica added, pointing to the growing piece in the girl's hands.

At that, the dark cloud passed, and the sun really came out, seeming to light the girl up from within.

For a couple more minutes, she chatted with Erica while her needles clattered against each other, and by the end, she had completed a good many rows, with only a couple of mistakes here and there.

She held up her garter stitch piece with pride as the bell rang.

"Can I carry on after playtime?" she asked.

Erica wasn't sure.

"There are other children who want to have a go, so I'll have to ask Miss Sullivan. Perhaps you can work at your desk and just bring it to me if you get stuck."

Metiya nodded and her eyes sparkled.

"Do you think I'll ever get as good as you and be able to knit without looking? I bet you could knit in your sleep!"

Erica laughed.

"Well, I wouldn't go that far, but I have been doing it since before I was your age." She leaned in and whispered. "Not that I'm going to tell anyone how many years ago that was!"

* * * *

In the staff room, Yvonne brought Erica a cup of tea.

"I'd love to know what magic spell you've cast over Metiya. She's normally so shy. It looked like there was a proper little knit and natter going on there this morning."

"It's funny how sharing handicrafts often loosens tongues," Erica replied.

She went on to tell her friend what Metiya had shared with her and Yvonne was very grateful, saying that she'd mention it to their pastoral care assistant when she was in next week.

"Oscar was excited to show me his knitting earlier, Mrs Marsh," Miss Sullivan called across the staff room. "He was asking if we could have a lunchtime knitting club in school.

"How about it?"

"You were looking for some volunteering to do on a regular basis, weren't you?" Yvonne piped up before Erica got the chance to answer. "And knitting is quiet and civilised."

"I'm not sure how relaxing it would be in a room full of primary children, but knitting is a good stress relief . . ."

Erica was interrupted by the sound of the bell and the general groan that followed it.

"In that case, I think you might need to run a second club for the staff," Yvonne said.

Erica was swept along in the boisterous tide of children jostling in from the playground to their respective classrooms, finishing snacks, jokes, games and arguments as they went.

Getting settled in her corner, she picked up a pair of needles and began casting on some stitches ready for the next pupil.

*   *   *   *

"Mrs Marsh, let me introduce Joel and Rafal. Normally, these two are the best of friends, but they've had a falling-out at playtime – something to do with the rules of a game.

Desert Island Dreams

If ever I should shipwrecked be, borne beachward by a wave,
As I surveyed the sinking craft, I wonder what I'd save?
Well, first upon my list of course, my choice of eight CDs,
The Bible and all Shakespeare's works, but what else would I seize?
A hammock and a parasol, well, that would be quite nice,
A crate of something good to drink, some lemons and some ice.
A tube of top-range sun-tan cream to stop me turning red,
A beach-towel and a pile of books, a cushion for my head.
And there upon my desert isle I'd sadly stay and mope
Till rescued by a passing ship — but not too soon, I hope!

Maggie Ingall.

"I can't seem to get to the bottom of it."

Miss Sullivan stood behind the boys and rolled her eyes at Erica.

"After what we were talking about in the staff room, I thought knitting might be just the thing. After all, in wartime, we all have to do our bit."

Horrified at the idea of being left in charge of this situation, Erica was about to suggest they might be better off on the painting table with Yvonne, but Miss Sullivan was already on her way to rejoin her reading group.

Looking from one scowling face to the other, Erica decided that arming disgruntled ten-year-olds with sharp knitting needles straight away might easily end in disaster, so she got them both unravelling an old sweater and balling up the yarn.

They were fascinated by the wiggly wool and the rhythm of the task must have smoothed their ruffled feathers.

Her mother's motto, "least said, soonest mended", came to mind, for very quickly the boys were having fun together, racing to see who could make the biggest ball of wool.

A while later, Miss Sullivan clapped her hands sharply to get everyone's attention.

"OK, class, you've all done brilliantly. Now, it's time to pack away so we can have our singalong."

She pressed a button on the remote control in her hand and then called across to Yvonne.

71

"Mrs Walker, can you check that the switch over there by the speakers is on, please?"

Yvonne turned the speaker switches on and off to no avail.

"We've got the piano in the hall. Only thing is, nobody on the staff can play it," Yvonne said. "Mind you, Mrs Marsh can, if I remember rightly."

Erica swallowed, her eyes widening at her friend.

"It's been a long while, and I'd have to have something to play from."

Miss Sullivan immediately started rummaging through some paperwork on her desk, excited.

"I'm sure it must be like riding a bike, Mrs Marsh, and we've got some simple sheet music right here in our resource pack.

"OK, class, line up quietly at the door! We're off to the hall."

∗　∗　∗　∗

"That was such a fun day, but I'm exhausted! How on earth do you do it full time?" Erica and Yvonne made their way along the corridor at half past three, aiming for coffee and cake at Huckleberries.

"It seems you won the war in Year Five today, Yvonne." A jovial man with a booming voice came out of the office door.

"Don't we always? This is my friend Erica. She's been helping us make do and mend."

Erica returned the head teacher's greeting and shook the hand he proffered.

"Always lovely to have new volunteers in school. Was it you I heard playing the piano earlier?"

"Sorry, Geoff, gotta go, now. Erica's got grandchildren." Yvonne bustled her friend out of the door. "See you tomorrow."

"What was that about?" Erica asked as they got settled in Yvonne's car.

"It's one thing me taking advantage of our friendship for the benefit of my class. It's something entirely different, you getting stuck playing for singing assembly every week!" Yvonne exclaimed.

Erica shrugged and sighed as she did up her seatbelt.

"Well, he's bound to ask again when he sees me, so it might be easier for me to brush up on my piano skills than sneak around the school hiding from him all the time."

Her friend stopped reversing the car to look at her through narrowed eyes.

"Does that mean knitting club's going ahead?"

Erica nodded.

"Although I'll want some more inspiring colours than beige and grey!"

Yvonne laughed.

"I should have warned you that setting foot inside a school as a volunteer is a dangerous business. You come for one small project and, six months on, you're part of the fabric of the place!"

"Well, I'm glad you persuaded me to take the risk." Erica smiled. "Although this afternoon, Mrs Walker, the coffees are definitely on you!" ■

Puffin

THE Atlantic puffin arrives in the UK in springtime and sets up home in the cliff faces and islands hugging our coastline. These striking looking birds are also known as sea parrots.

Their brightly coloured faces and strange waddle on land have earned them the nickname "clowns of the sea", and as well as an improbability or a puffinry, a circus is one of their collective names.

Belonging to the auk family, these seabirds have breeding colonies in a few areas of the UK, including Orkney and Shetland, the Isle of May, Fife and the Farne Islands. Their young are called pufflings.

Their parrot-like beaks change colour depending on the season, from a dull colour in winter through to vivid orange in summer.

Puffins' bills are great for holding a multitude of small fish such as sprats, and they also love to eat sand eels, herring and cod.

From reaching up to 55 mph in the skies, puffins are also expert divers. It's estimated they eat an average 40 small fish a day. ■

Taking Control

by Alison Carter

M AXINE MORAN wasn't even sure why she was in this meeting, but Mr Robertson had given her a "look" as he passed her desk with a client, and so she had followed him. Maxine had been surprised that Mr Robertson even knew who she was, because she had only just started at his firm.

Mr Robertson did not seem happy with what the client was saying.

"Yes, Geoffrey, we have always used your marketing services, but now Darston Sidney Toiletries is branching out.

"We want to move into advertising our own wares."

"Are you dissatisfied with the work of Robertson and Sons?" Mr Robertson asked.

"No, no. This change in no way involves criticism."

Mr Robertson hesitated.

"You know how much is involved in marketing, Mr Sidney?"

Maxine could see from her boss's face that he was sure the client had no idea whatsoever.

She knew that Darston Sidney made corn plasters, knee supports and the like.

Mr Sidney now laced his fingers together.

"Oh, yes, but my people know our products! No disrespect to your firm, of course.

"My daughter, for instance, is fresh out of college with a qualification in history of art, and keen to bring in ideas."

Mr Robertson was trying to keep a straight face.

Young people just out of college with a qualification in history of art were banned from Robertson and Sons.

Mr Robertson said they only ever wanted to be the next Renoir, or worse, the next Jackson Pollock, and were no use.

Maxine had succeeded in getting her job after two years in a packaging design firm, and lots of practical experience.

Set in 1967

Illustration by Gerard Fay.

Maxine was sent back to her desk, and half an hour later Mr Robertson came to find her.

"I pulled you in there to give a good impression to a shaky client," he said with a sigh.

"I thought a pretty girl might . . . but to no avail. What's your name, again?"

"Maxine Moran."

"Oh, yes."

"I gave him a whisky, and then another, and he talked more about the daughter.

"He's not as silly as he looks. He's spotted that letting her loose on the brand might not be without issues." He rolled his eyes.

"History of art!" He smiled.

"I've promised him a minder."

"A what, Mr Robertson?"

"To help the girl. You start over there on Monday. Clearly, I wasn't about to release anyone important for this."

"Clearly," Maxine said very quietly.

"He's going to keep his account with us open and pay us – you – to keep an eye on the daughter.

"It's a good move. Take it from me – Darston Sidney will be back.

"They will be hopeless at marketing and will return with their tail between their legs."

*   *   *   *

This was not the step up that Maxine had dreamed of since leaving college in 1964.

She headed home that evening with a bit of paper from Mr Robertson giving "details".

You're a Girl Friday, it said. *Don't try to one-up the daughter. She thinks you're employed as a sort of favour to an "old friend". Just let Dad know if things go awry.*

Maxine laid the bit of paper on the sideboard of her tiny Salford flat, and went downstairs to the hall to ring Luke, her friend since school.

Luke had been the heart-throb at Kentonwick High School and the boy every girl wanted to go out with.

Maxine had been his ally, the one he laughed with about all the other girls and the one who reliably didn't bat her eyelids at him.

Other people thought it an odd relationship. Nowadays, he worked as a model.

When Maxine's friend Beatrice from her job at the packaging company met Luke, she assumed they were a couple.

"You lucky devil!" Beatrice exclaimed. "He's gorgeous!"

Maxine laughed.

"Me and Luke? No chance!"

Beatrice pouted.

"So, he's got a girlfriend elsewhere? I've never seen a man as good-looking, not in real life."

"He's single, Beatrice."

Beatrice gaped.

"You are telling me that Luke, model and dish of the day, is unattached, that he spends a couple of evenings a week with you −"

"And we go to Man City games. We're fans."

"But there's nothing . . . like that going on?"

Maxine shrugged.

"We're mates."

"You're crazy."

But Maxine knew how far out of her league her friend Luke was.

*　*　*　*

On only her first day at Darston Sidney, Maxine found out just how enthusiastic Harriet Sidney was.

She was a tall, sporty-looking woman of about twenty-five, with a long blonde ponytail and a strong nose.

She had the look of a boarding-school girl, all hockey sticks and horses.

That day Maxine was wearing an orange mini skirt and woolly tights, wanting to look smart on her first day.

She loved fashion although she didn't have much cash.

Beside Harriet's tweed skirt and pale silk blouse she felt young and outclassed.

"I'm sure you're good at what you do, Maxine," Harriet Sidney said, "but Daddy can send you back to your other work shortly − I have a good grip on this."

She slid a cardboard box across the desk between them.

"Shaving," she said firmly, "the glamorous end of the product range."

The box was a mock-up, and a very bad one.

The lid kept bouncing open, it wobbled, and somebody had corrected the text on the front with an ink pen.

"The Adonis Shaving Kit," Harriet said.

"This is going to be the thing that brings this company up to date!"

"Right," Maxine said. "So we – you – are repackaging –"

"Bundling!" Harriet cried.

"That's the new word. Safety razor, soap, brush, leaflet. Something for the modern man to get his teeth into."

Maxine smiled.

"That sounds nasty," she said.

"Sorry?"

"Teeth into shaving soap? I had a vision of foaming mou –"

"I need a concept," Harriet interrupted, not getting the joke.

"I want fresh colours, a whole identity." She stood up and grabbed a stack of magazines from a side table.

"What does the new man want, and with what does he identify?" She stared hard at Maxine.

"Go with me on my journey, since you're here. Men!"

"Er." Maxine didn't want to laugh, but it was hard not to. "Um, well . . . think of the men you know."

"Daddy?"

"I was thinking more of your target market." Maxine took the box.

"I'm guessing it's younger than Mr Sidney? Think of men you've gone on dates with, for instance."

Harriet's large frame grew still. She looked at the magazines and then laid them on the desk and straightened the edges of the stack.

"Well, obviously," she said.

Maxine knew immediately that Harriet had never had a boyfriend.

"I'm just wondering," Maxine said. An idea was coming to her.

"How about one particular man? For the product."

Harriet's eyes widened.

"A face of the brand! Like the Pears Soap girl, or Oxo Katie!"

Maxine was tremendously pleased with herself.

It was obvious that this was a job for Luke! He would be ideal, and Maxine could do him a huge favour in the process.

Luke had been barely earning a living via dull catalogue jobs, smiling in endless Crimplene wash-'n'-wear shirts.

He was hard-working and good at dealing with a tricky client.

Luke had been obliged to fight for a modelling career because, in 1967, his looks were unusual.

His father was a black American GI now settled in south Manchester, and his mum was an Old Trafford girl.

Maxine looked narrowly at Harriet, as if sizing her up. She needed to take Miss Sidney of Darston Sidney along with her.

"I think you are the sort of person, Harriet, who is willing to try going to the cutting edge," she said.

"Oh, yes," Harriet breathed. "I am."

"I have a contact," Maxine said. "A professional model you might want to take a look at."

* * * *

It was hilarious when Harriet met Luke.

Since the age of sixteen, when he'd attained six feet one and acquired a set of muscles, Maxine had seen jaws drop at the sight of Luke, but Harriet's reaction was special.

She turned into a flustered mess of pink-faced embarrassment.

"Sit down, please," she said. "Coffee? Tea? Hot milk?" She giggled loudly and then had to cough.

"Nobody drinks hot milk at work! I think we have sherry. Do we have sherry, Maxine? Oh, you've only just started so you won't know!

"It's nice to meet you, Mr Luke. Luke. Mr Luke Masters.

"It's good – I mean it's good in a professional way –"

She fell silent for a few seconds before taking a gulped breath.

"Please, sit down."

They had only got as far as reception and there was only one chair.

Luke took her hand and shook it in his calm, easy way.

He flashed her his wonderful smile with its row of pearly teeth, and Maxine saw Harriet crumple like a flannel dropping into a bath.

She glanced at Luke.

They shared an acute understanding of the world, and enjoyed laughing at idiotic people and crazy things.

Often, it only took a quick look between them to remind Maxine that as long as she had Luke in her life, there would always be fun.

Harriet sensed the receptionist watching them.

"Nosey Noreen", as she was known.

"Tea would be lovely," Luke said, smiling gently at Harriet.

"Tea!" Harriet shouted. She set off at an actual run for the kitchen, her string of pearls banging against her chest.

There was a pause while Luke and Maxine watched her go.

"Are you two a couple?" Noreen asked, fixing a covetous gaze at Luke. He burst out laughing. The sharpness of the sound made Maxine jump.

"Us? Good grief no!" he said. "We've never . . . no."

"No," Maxine added. This time there was no shared glance. They were both looking at Noreen, who shrugged.

"I'll take you to Harriet's office," Maxine said quickly.

This mistake had been made before – this making of assumptions about the two of them.

But the idea of her being "with" Luke was ridiculous.

And anyway, her family would never speak to her again if she went out with Luke in that way.

She remembered a horrible moment, years ago, when she had taken Luke home from school.

They had been rehearsing something – a play, or maybe a concert.

They both found themselves thirsty and the Moran house was nearby.

As soon as Luke stepped into the hall, and Maxine saw her father's hard, suspicious expression, and her mother's visible discomfort, she knew that Luke represented something bad to them.

Since that day she had wondered if her family's ignorance had cemented their friendship, at least from her point of view.

Maxine struggled with her family and felt herself to be an outsider.

But it had always been friendship.

There had been another, very different moment, after a New Year dance when they were eighteen.

They had run outside for air and the cold had hit them.

Luke had hugged her and they had stayed like that, wrapped around each other, until he loosened his grip and then . . .

But that night had been an anomaly.

One day he would get engaged to an actress or a beautiful model, or somebody very rich.

He would meet those sorts of girls more and more in his job.

Maxine was short and curvy; her hair was uncontrollably curly and looked stupid if she tried to tame it under her favourite Brigitte Bardot hairband. Her legs were as short as the rest of her.

It was always going to be friendship.

* * * *

Harriet looked like a love-sick puppy with Luke, but in between giggling, rearranging her ponytail and paying him compliments, she got on with the job.

One afternoon the two women were supposed to be visiting a printer about the shaving kit boxes, but the appointment was delayed.

They decided to make tea, and made their way to the kitchen-lounge on the floor above, but as they walked along the corridor they heard Mr Sidney talking to his finance manager inside.

"She's a lovely girl," Mr Sidney was saying. "We adore her, Marcy and I, but that expensive girls' school hasn't cured her gawkiness, and it seems to have given her ideas about women's liberation."

"She wants to work, Trevor."

He chuckled.

"I've got her pottering on a product line, to keep her happy while she tracks down a husband."

"Let's go," Maxine whispered, but Harriet remained glued to the spot as her father carried on.

"She's hired a coloured fellow as a . . . what do they call it? As a 'face' for one of our lines." Maxine could hear the smile in his voice.

"It's to shock me." He laughed, and there was a clink of glass.

"And it was the little girl from our old marketing company that got the chap on board, not really Harriet.

"I'm happy with the model chappy, though. A fellow like that might attract a younger market."

Harriet turned on her heel and walked away.

Maxine heard nothing about the incident until a day later.

"I'm having doubts about Luke. I've been thinking about going even further with the idea of the new face," Harriet said.

Maxine's heart sank. What was coming?

"I went to the cinema last night," she said, "with a school pal. I saw a Marlon Brando."

"Lovely," Maxine said.

"Marlon is from Nebraska with the endless fields, the wide sky.

"His father sold feed – did you know that? He came from nothing; he was one of those actors who represent the American dream of rising to the top.

"Making a real 'discovery' will have a huge impact on the campaign. A country boy, say, wet behind the ears." She brightened.

"I can see it now! An amateur model discovers the sophistication of a slick city shave! Maybe even some television ads, with a story."

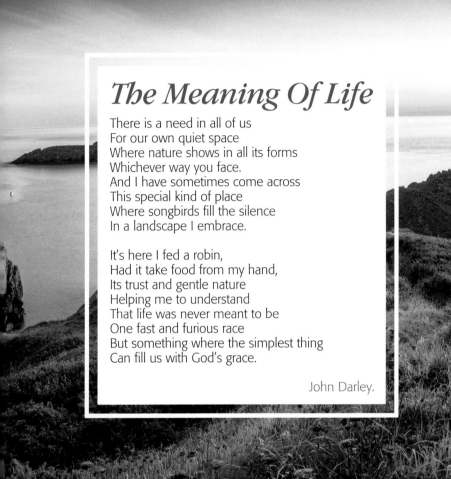

The Meaning Of Life

There is a need in all of us
For our own quiet space
Where nature shows in all its forms
Whichever way you face.
And I have sometimes come across
This special kind of place
Where songbirds fill the silence
In a landscape I embrace.

It's here I fed a robin,
Had it take food from my hand,
Its trust and gentle nature
Helping me to understand
That life was never meant to be
One fast and furious race
But something where the simplest thing
Can fill us with God's grace.

John Darley.

"I think Luke could achieve what you envisage –"

"Luke is great, obviously."

Maxine could see the memory of him playing on Harriet's face.

"But business is business, and a brilliant idea carries everything along with it. I'd expect you to know that."

Maxine could see that Harriet was determined to make her own mark, and have her father understand that she was not a child.

This was bad news for Luke and Maxine felt terrible.

He was broke, his rent long overdue. He had been hanging on, waiting for his first payslip from Darston Sidney, but had done no actual work on the project except meetings and a photography test.

He was horrified.

"I have to keep hold of this job, Max. How do I convince her?"

"Well, she likes you." As soon as she spoke, Maxine regretted it.

"Likes me as in, likes me?"

"I don't know. Maybe." It amazed Maxine that he hadn't noticed.

"Make up your mind." His eyes bored into her.

"If she likes me, is it all right with you if I try that as an approach?"

Maxine looked at the floor.

"Why would it not be?" She felt unexpectedly angry. "It's an advantage that she likes you, isn't it?"

Luke was getting worked up.

"So her dad is a problem? I can offer a shoulder to cry on."

Maxine wanted to go home. She and Luke had been going for fish and chips, but she wasn't hungry any more.

She knew she was being silly; it was nothing to do with her if he chatted up Harriet Sidney, or if he chatted up anybody.

Luke had never introduced her to girlfriends; it was an unspoken rule that they kept their friendship clear of that stuff.

"I bet I can reel her back in," he said. "She's a nice girl."

Maxine had seen women in coffee bars slide down in their Formica chairs while listening to Luke merely talk about the weather.

To woo Harriet back to her original decision, Luke did his research.

"Noreen on reception says she loves lilies," he told Maxine.

"She always comments on lilies on the desk."

So Luke bought lilies for Harriet.

"I told her it was a 'no hard feelings about the contract' thing," he told Maxine. "In the card I said I hoped to see her soon."

Luke began to report back to Maxine on his progress.

There was a trip to the funfair "just like two teenagers", and a barefoot picnic in the sun.

"All women love to be taken on a picnic," Luke said.

"I hate ants," Maxine said. She felt grumpy, and wished she could go back to Robertson's and work on something else.

Luke bought Harriet more lilies, and took her to the Henley Regatta. By all accounts they had a wonderful time.

"Henley's a posh girl's heaven," he told Maxine.

"I also had a brainwave and told her about my dad's origins in working class Detroit sheet metal, and my mum's cotton millworkers heritage.

"I can be the boy from nowhere!"

"Your dad's family run an insurance business and your mum was a hairdresser before she got married."

He grinned.

"But it's working! I told her that spending time with her is not about the work any more. I was vague — I don't want to be too obvious.

"I said I loved her idea of a non-professional model. I said it shows she's got brave ideas."

Maxine didn't like what Luke was doing but she wasn't sure why.

He was obviously good at it, and she felt sure that Harriet could be convinced, and the plan for Luke's success could be put back on.

But she hated the enthusiasm with which he went about the task, and the pleasure Harriet clearly got from it.

Maxine and Luke met one evening for a beer.

"I got a one-day job on a catalogue," he said. "I'll take you to the Midland Hotel for a treat."

Luke stopped dead in the entrance to the bar, and Maxine crashed into his back.

"What?" she asked.

"It's Harriet."

As Maxine peered round him, she saw that Harriet had noticed them, and was beckoning.

She was seated at a table beside a fair-haired man in a blazer and striped university tie.

As Maxine and Luke approached, the man gave Harriet an enquiring look. Maxine wondered if he was Harriet's brother.

"And who is this?" the man asked.

"Colleagues," Harriet said. "Giles, this is Luke and Maxine."

"Lovely to meet you," Giles said. "What can I get you? And another orange juice for you, darling?"

Luke and Maxine shared the briefest of stunned glances.

"Lovely," Harriet said, and Giles headed for the bar.

"I'm not quite as easy to manipulate as you imagine," Harriet said with a smile. "Please, sit down.

"I look like a girl from the Chalet School but I'm not quite an idiot.

"Luke, I've had a jolly nice time on the picnics and the big wheel, and you are delightful. I have tried not to be insulted at being patronised."

Luke and Maxine were dumbstruck.

"You two are a team," Harriet went on.

"You understand each other like the earth understands the moon, and that makes you think that you understand everybody else.

"But I've been gaining my own confidence since starting at the firm.

"I'm not sure if I'll stay at Darston Sidney – that depends on my father taking me seriously.

"But I take myself seriously, and I know I can do the job." She regarded them steadily.

"And make decisions." She looked across the expanse of patterned carpet. "I met Giles at Henley, actually."

Luke was staring at Giles as he handed over a note to the barman.

"He's super," Harriet said, "and doesn't mind me being new to the dating game."

Still, neither Maxine nor Luke spoke, and Harriet looked from one to the other.

"I saw straight away that you're in love with each other, as soon as I stopped being awkward around Luke's godlike good looks.

"I could have been a nun, or a dormouse, and still spotted that."

Maxine's head twitched.

Her instinct would normally cause her to look at Luke and share the moment, and pass an identical opinion silently back and forth.

But how could she do that now, when the truth was pouring out of Harriet's mouth?

"It has been funnier and funnier," Harriet said, "seeing how Luke would woo me next, but he has no interest in me, except that I can give him work.

"How long have you been in love with Maxine, Luke? About as long as Maxine has loved you?"

It had been Harriet in control of the situation for a long time!

It was Maxine and Luke whose motivations and weaknesses were laid wide open.

Maxine felt foolish.

She also felt keyed up with nerves. She did love Luke, and always had.

"He's out of my league," Maxine said in a voice that even she could hardly hear.

"Sorry?" Harriet said.

"Let's go," Luke said, and Maxine felt her hand being taken, and herself led out on to Peter Street and into a summer night.

"I thought you were falling for her," Maxine said to his back as he dragged her away from the grand front of the hotel.

He turned round.

"That is the maddest thing I have ever heard," he said. "Her? When I know you?"

They looked at each other for half a minute.

"I've had enough sharing understanding glances with you," Luke said. "I'm going to kiss you instead."

Quite a long time later he asked, "What about your mum and dad?"

"What about them?" she said. "They don't rule me. What about your career?"

"That comes second to this." And he kissed her again.

In the end, Harriet decided that Luke was right for the Adonis campaign.

She admitted that her change of direction had been an attempt to make her father take notice, and finally he did.

"It's not a good reflection on him," Harriet said, "that it took introducing Giles to make him realise that I'm not twelve any more.

"But he looked at my work, and admitted that I know my stuff.

"So, thanks, Maxine, for your part in this, and I'll be writing you a marvellous reference to take back to Robertson's.

"Dad is restarting the account, by the way — he's spotted that there are not too many marketing experts to be had at Darston Sidney, apart from his daughter."

"I think you can run with this one," Maxine said. "It's going to be great."

"I've rethought the box."

"Oh, yes," Maxine said with a laugh, "that."

Harriet turned to Luke.

"So, be at the studio at noon on Tuesday.

"You're back, but try not to send the account executive — that's me — any more lilies.

"I've seen enough lilies for a lifetime." ■

York, Yorkshire

As this city dates back to AD 71, many of York's thoroughfares were not constructed with motor vehicles in mind. These lanes rejoice in the name of "snickelways", a term coined by Mark W. Jones in his 1983 guide, "A Walk Around The Snickelways Of York". The term means a narrow passageway linking two different places.

Following Mark's map, you will stroll along York's Shambles, first mentioned in the Domesday Book, and wander along the delightfully named "Whip-Ma-Whop-Ma-Gate",which started life in 1505 as "Whitnourwhatnourgate", meaning "what a street".

The walk begins and ends at York Minster, a beautiful Gothic cathedral. Begun in 1080 and completed 400 years later, the stunning craftsmanship attracts visitors from all over the world.

Thankfully, there are still artisans practising the craft of their mediaeval predecessors, from stonework to stained-glass windows, who help to keep the Minster in the fine condition it enjoys today.

Four Weddings And A Cake

by Eirin Thompson

YOU could say I was allergic to weddings. I didn't like the cake, I didn't like dancing and most of all I didn't like brides who spent more than a year planning and making lists and shopping and fretting over a single day.

And I should know – I'm the youngest of five sisters.

When Ruthanne, the eldest, got engaged, Mum cried.

"That's the start of it, girls – one by one you're all going to leave me."

Dad was more pragmatic, saying it would take the pressure off the immersion heater to the tune of one-fifth.

Ruthanne said she'd been planning her wedding in her head since she'd been a little girl.

No sooner did she have the diamond ring on her finger than she started traipsing round all the bridal salons looking for the Dress.

Mum went with her the first time, but Ruthanne wasn't satisfied with that. The next week we all had to tag along.

Rebecca, Ruby and Rachel seemed to enjoy the experience. I cannot imagine why – it was so tedious.

I sat in the corner with a Biro drawing beards and moustaches on the brides in the glossy brochure.

"Riley! Don't be so childish!" Ruthanne snapped.

"Don't look at me," I retorted. "You're the one playing dress-up."

We looked at approximately 500 wedding dresses, some full and frothy, some slim and sleek, some with puffed sleeves, some with none, before Ruthanne announced that she'd like to go back and see the one

Illustration by Martin Baines.

she'd tried on the very first day.

And that was the one she bought.

Once the Dress had been chosen, Ruthanne wasted no time in seeking bridesmaids' gowns that would complement it.

"Anything but pink," Ruby pleaded. "I can't do pink, with my red hair."

"I was wondering about oyster," Ruthanne said. "What do you think?"

"Have you ever seen an oyster?" I queried. "It's the colour of phlegm."

"Oh, Riley!" Ruthanne cried. "Tell her to shut up, Mum. She has to spoil everything."

"Listen, I'll happily leave you to it," I said.

"Oh, no, you won't," Ruthanne insisted. "I need to know that whatever frock I choose suits all four of you."

Trying to get four girls to agree on the one dress that looked good on everybody was a tall order.

Ruby didn't like people to see her freckly shoulders. Rebecca begged for a style that gave her a flat tummy and Rachel was very proud of her collarbones and wanted them displayed to best advantage.

"It seems to me that the emerald green with the Fifties-style bodice has more or less chosen itself, and it sits well with my bride's dress," Ruthanne declared at last. "That OK with you, Riley?"

"Whatever."

After all that, I thought maybe the wedding plans would go on the back burner for a bit.

But no – it was shopping for shoes, seeing round possible venues, selecting all three courses of the menu, choosing the hymns, designing the order of service, making choices about flowers and favours and – a tough one – whom to invite and whom to offend.

Ruthanne couldn't do any of this alone – we all had to be involved.

"Where's Ralph in all this?" I ventured to ask, as we were gathered round the kitchen table poring over the seating plan. "Shouldn't the groom be a bit more involved?"

"Ralph's very busy with work," Ruthanne answered. "Don't be so miserable, Riley. I'd have loved to have had a big sister getting married. There's nothing as exciting as a wedding."

The big day came and I dutifully had my hair curled and my make-up applied, I wore the green dress and the shoes and did my best to smile.

But I was stuck on the very end of the top table for the meal, beside an usher who talked to Rachel on his other side, so that wasn't fun.

I worked my way through the meal in silence, yawned during the speeches and, when the dancing started, I sneaked upstairs to the room Ruthanne had set aside for wardrobe, hair and make-up adjustments, lay down and fell asleep.

Nobody missed me.

When it was all over, I felt great.

Back to normality, at last. Except, within a year, Rebecca announced that Johnny had proposed and she was thinking about it.

And the whole palaver started again.

I didn't kid myself. Ruby would be next. Correct.

And then Rachel came home flashing a diamond. Hers would be my fourth wedding as a sister and bridesmaid in five years.

It sounds ungrateful, I know. But, like I said, I'm allergic to weddings.

∗   ∗   ∗   ∗

By the time Rachel's nuptials came along, I had been promoted to chief bridesmaid.

The other sisters were married – Ruthanne with two little children, Rebecca with one and Ruby just weeks off going into labour.

"It's very important," Rachel kept reminding me. "The chief bridesmaid is the bride's right-hand woman – there's a lot of responsibility."

This time the bride was wearing an Edwardian-style lacy affair and the bridesmaids were in taupe.

"Do you love your dress?" Rachel asked excitedly.

"No," I said.

I think even Mum was getting a bit wedding-weary, this time around.

"Couldn't you borrow Ruby's shoes?" she asked Rachel. "She's only worn them once. They could be your something borrowed."

"I knew this would happen!" Rachel wailed. "Just because I'm the fourth sister, nobody even cares. I want my own special shoes for my own special day.

"And don't you look so uninterested, Riley – by the time it's your turn you'll probably have to get married in a flour sack and have your reception in McDonald's."

"Trust me, it'll never be my turn," I assured her. "I have no intention of ever getting married."

* * * *

It was the Thursday before Rachel's big day and time for the wedding rehearsal. We all congregated at the church, which was the first time our family had met some of the groom's guests.

We knew Carlton's mum and dad, of course, and I'd been introduced to his sister, Annette, who was also a bridesmaid, when we'd been dress-shopping.

"Guy can't make the rehearsal," Carlton explained. "But Edward is going to stand in as best man, just for now."

Edward was Carlton's kid brother, all of four feet tall. He looked about as delighted about rehearsing a wedding as I felt.

We stood around, being lined up and turned this way and that, then the men went inside, and we girls followed Rachel up the aisle.

There was a bit more palaver with the rector saying things, and Carlton and Rachel responding. I wasn't paying very much attention.

"Riley? Riley! Will you take those ear-buds out, please?"

Busted. I hadn't thought anyone would notice.

"This is where you help me turn my dress and train and we all process back down the aisle," Rachel commanded.

What, was I actually supposed to mime turning round an Edwardian gown when Rachel was wearing jeggings and a T-shirt?

"Well come on, don't just stand there!"

Apparently I was.

"Now the wedding party in pairs, behind us!" Rachel called. "And each pair holding hands, please."

I looked at Edward. He looked at me. Reluctantly, we took each other's hands. He was so much shorter than me it actually made me walk with a limp.

* * * *

Rachel looked radiant, if you liked that sort of thing.

She glided up the aisle on Dad's arm, Ruthanne up ahead, coaching her little girl to toss rose petals on the floor, Annette and me bringing up the rear.

Glancing up, I saw Carlton standing with his hands behind his back, facing the altar. To his right was a tall figure with a head of dark shaggy hair. This must be Guy, the best man.

I thought he'd done well to get away with those long locks – Rachel would have been trying to have them cut, no doubt.

Rachel arrived at the front of the church, the organ music stopped and the ceremony began.

I stifled a yawn and thought about how I'd escape the dancing later. I could say I had a headache – sometimes simple plans were the best.

I admit, I drifted away somewhat during the ceremony, but I woke right up when Rachel glared at me and I realised it was time to perform the big turn of the Edwardian dress and train to enable the retreat.

"I've got this, I've got this," I assured her.

We turned, we fell into pairs, and I felt someone grasp my hand.

"Hello. You must be Riley. I'm Guy."

Guy was, no kidding, tall, dark and handsome. We stood for a second, as Rachel and Carlton prepared to move.

I was just about to say it was nice to meet him, when my stomach gave an enormous grumble and my niece with the basket of petals piped up.

"What was that noise, Mummy?"

"Hungry?" Guy enquired, a twinkle in his eye.

I felt myself blush furiously.

"Breakfast was a long time ago."

"I understand there are to be canapés on arrival at the hotel – think you can hang on?"

"Of course."

✳ ✳ ✳ ✳

I was standing in the corner with my plate piled high – five or six little potato cakes with smoked salmon and cream cheese and half a dozen mini avocado toasts. Yum.

"Riley?"

It was Guy. Trust him to show up when my cheeks were stuffed like a greedy hamster.

"Mhmm?"

"Sorry to interrupt your lunch." His eyes were twinkling again, I noticed. "But Rachel wants us for the photographs."

I gulped down what was in my mouth and must have looked at my stacked plate in dismay.

"We can bring them with us," Guy said, grabbing my plate in one hand and my hand in his other. "But we do have to go out to the courtyard."

He hurried me along and soon we were lining up for the camera.

Rachel insisted on photographs of every possible combination of the bridal party, but each time the best man and chief bridesmaid weren't needed, Guy appeared beside me with my plate.

"You're welcome to share," I told him.

"So, which sister are you?" Guy asked, while all the parents were being photographed with the happy couple. "The one with two children, or the one with the baby, or the expectant one? Not that you're showing."

"I'm the one on the shelf."

"On the shelf? Really?"

"Yes. And I happen to like it there. Or I will do once all these blooming weddings are over and everybody leaves me alone."

"You're not keen on being a bridesmaid, then?"

"I wasn't keen when Ruthanne got married, and now this is my fourth. So no."

"But I thought young women loved all this – getting dressed up, the pomp and ceremony and romance."

"It's a lot of fuss over a dress and a big dinner."

"That's really how you see it?"

"It is."

"Well, that's just terrible."

Someone from the hotel function room appeared then, and said they really couldn't delay the meal any longer and would the bride and groom please leave any further photographs until later.

"At last," I said.

At the top table, Guy was surprisingly good company.

Over our starter of butternut and lemongrass soup, he managed to coax me into telling him about my job selling advertising on a newspaper and my ambition to break into journalism.

"It'll mean going to evening classes after work, to learn shorthand and typing," I explained.

"If you're determined, you'll find the extra energy," Guy said.

He told me that he was a graphic designer, working for a solid company, but tempted to branch out on his own.

"That'll take a lot of extra energy, too," I surmised.

"And now for the inevitable breast of chicken wrapped in parma ham." I sighed, eyeing the plate that had been set before me.

"But not just any breast of chicken wrapped in Parma ham," Guy pointed out. "Didn't you read the menu? This one's stuffed with chorizo and tarragon and finished with Madeira jus, not to mention the side of Dauphinoise potatoes, which are my absolute favourite."

I had to smile.

As we polished off our desserts, Guy was telling me of his plans to get a rescue dog and I was warning him about the heartache of losing it one day, as we'd recently lost Wuzzins, our family cat.

"But it doesn't make you wish you'd never had him," Guy suggested.

"Oh, no. He brought us a great deal of joy down the years. We wouldn't have missed that for the world. 'It's better to have loved and lost than never to have loved at all'."

Guy put his head on one side.

"It's nice to hear you say that," he remarked.

And before I could bite back my words and assure him that my statement only applied to pets, and that I didn't have a romantic bone in my body, he was up on his feet, tapping an empty glass with a knife, signalling the start of the speeches.

These began as the usual yawnfest. If I wasn't very much mistaken, Dad had copied and pasted his script from various earlier weddings, although luckily Rachel didn't seem to notice.

The groom's words were as dull as ditchwater.

But then it was Guy's turn, and I found myself listening intently.

He related one or two tales of youthful frolics with Carlton, his deep affection for the groom's family and of how he and Carlton had stayed in touch all through uni, though they were hundreds of miles apart.

Then he explained how he'd had to adjust to Carlton meeting Rachel, who had quickly become the centre of his universe, but how Guy had been happy, because Carlton was so evidently happy.

He wove in quotes and kept the room spellbound. When he proposed his toast to the bride and groom, everyone stood up and cheered.

But Guy hadn't quite finished.

"It's traditional, I understand, for the best man to thank the bridesmaids for their contribution to a wonderful day. As well as asking you to raise your glasses to the bridesmaids, I have the happy task of singling out one bridesmaid in particular.

"Riley Robinson is chief bridesmaid today, but not everyone will know that she has performed the role of bridesmaid for all four of her sisters and they have asked me to present her with this gift, in recognition of her outstanding service."

I gripped my napkin in surprise. I'd been the worst bridesmaid ever!

"Stand up, Riley!" Rachel growled.

I stood.

Guy handed me a velvet box. He'd known which sister I was all along.

"Open it," Ruthanne called from a nearby table.

Inside was a beautiful silver pendant and matching earrings – kind of traditional, but in a design that I really liked.

"Thank you," I murmured.

Feeling my eyes brimming, I plonked myself back down on my chair.

* * * *

The staff were moving the tables back to the sides of the room to free up the floor for dancing.

"This is where I generally take off," I told Guy.

"What, you mean go home?" he asked.

"I'm not quite that brave," I admitted. "I generally try to find somewhere to sleep. There's usually a room set aside for people adjusting their gowns, or else I slip into the back seat of one of the hire cars – they're both roomy and comfortable."

"But you'll miss the dancing."

"That's the general idea."

"You don't like to dance?"

"I'm no good at it. I'm wooden."

"But you like music."

"Of course I do. I just can't move to it with any degree of grace."

"I bet you could dance with me."

I looked at Guy. Handsome, friendly, charming. Of course he'd be great on the dance-floor.

"I'd only embarrass you," I told him.

"I was right about the chicken – it was great. I'd like the chance to persuade you that all the things you claim to dislike about weddings might be a lot nicer than you think.

"Anyway, you can't leave before the couple have their first dance."

Maybe it was because this was the last of the weddings, maybe it was because I'd had so much fun talking that I'd avoided my usual sleepy head, maybe it was because Guy was so handsome and so nice, but before I knew it we were joining Rachel and Carlton on the floor.

I heard Ruthanne shriek.

"Look, Ralph! Is that really Riley up dancing?"

And, in truth, it wasn't so bad. Guy held me firmly, but not too tightly, and guided my every step. Then the DJ played a faster number and Guy swung me and spun me and I found myself smiling and laughing.

"Want to sit down?" he enquired, as that song came to an end.

"No! I want to stay up!" I cried.

We danced a couple more times, then Guy said he must have a turn with the bride, so I danced with the groom, which wasn't as good as dancing with Guy, but it wasn't awful.

I must have been on my feet for an hour, and loving every minute, until the DJ announced that the next dance was the "Hokey Cokey" and my wedding allergy kicked off again.

"I am not dancing the 'Hokey Cokey'," I told Guy.

"Agreed. I draw the line there, too," he replied. "Shall we slip outside for a bit? It's very warm in here."

On the hotel balcony, Guy said, "So, was today horrendous?"

"Not entirely," I conceded.

"I enjoy a wedding," Guy continued. "Music, pageantry, getting dressed up, a decent meal, dancing, meeting new people . . ."

"I'm glad I met you," I murmured, not daring to look at him.

"I'm very glad we met, too. Would it be all right if I kissed you?"

I had to think.

"Not if this is just a heat of the moment thing. Not if I'm never going to see you again."

"Of course I want to see you again." Guy sounded genuinely surprised. "You don't think I've put in all this effort getting to know you for nothing?

"I like you, Riley. You've got some funny ideas, but you intrigue me. And you're extremely pretty."

When we emerged from our embrace, Rebecca came thundering out.

"Everyone back inside! They've just remembered to cut the cake!"

"Fruitcake – yuk! That's one aspect of weddings you'll never change my mind about," I declared.

"I hate the stuff, too," Guy replied. "That's why my one proviso regarding being best man was that there had to be a tier of chocolate."

"And Rachel agreed?"

"I assured them it was a deal-breaker."

As we sat side by side eating chocolate cake, I thought I might have to update my allergy status.

Weddings weren't so bad, once you learned how to enjoy them. ■

She immediately regretted thinking such a thing, particularly when Gloria asked her if she had time for a coffee.

"Come on, let's splurge, they do a wonderful chocolate cake."

*   *   *   *

Standing in her potting shed later that afternoon, Eartha thought about her visit to the garden centre that morning.

Had Gloria overheard her waxing lyrical about how wonderful her front garden was going to be?

Maybe not, she thought. She certainly hadn't mentioned anything over coffee, though they had briefly discussed the village competition.

Best Front Garden. If only, Eartha thought. Three years now she'd been trying, and not so much as a glimmer. Gloria didn't even try, and last year, she'd scooped the gold!

Eartha thought back to last year and the hours she'd spent on her knees, digging weeds out of her lawn.

The more she dug out, the more they spread. Each time she lifted out a weed, another sneaked in and brought its friends along.

Later that afternoon, Eartha looked out at Gloria's lawn next door.

It was like a bowling green, a smooth, green sward that a snooker table would have been proud to display. There wasn't a weed in sight.

And Gloria never did a thing. It was as if she'd put up a sign saying, *Hi, there, weeds, slugs and other assorted pests, would you be kind enough not to use my garden? I want to win the competition. Thank you! P.S. There's plenty of room next door.*

In the potting shed, Eartha gave a long sigh and told herself off.

"Oh, bother," she said to the compost. "If only Gloria wasn't such a lovely friend and neighbour."

And a true friend she'd certainly been.

When Eartha had moved in, Gloria had been first on the doorstep to welcome her to the Crescent with some flowers and a delicious cake, and they'd quickly become firm friends and cooking buddies.

They had morning coffee whenever they could, and had walked their dogs together until Eartha had lost Ghillie, her beautiful golden retriever.

It was another time when Gloria had been such a comfort.

It's not as if I mind Gloria winning, Eartha told herself. I'm pleased for her. But it would be nice to win something, just once.

As she opened the chocolate biscuits, Eartha started to think. What does Gloria actually do?

The answer was staring her in the face.

Nothing. That's what Gloria did. Absolutely nothing.

Now and again, she ran a rusty old mower over the lawn and clipped the edges with a pair of scissors.

Once a year she stepped out with an equally rusty pair of shears and chopped at all the plants like a hedge.

On occasion, if they'd had a long, dry spell, she came out with a bucket of water and threw it in their general direction.

That was it. No food, no weeding, no nurturing – no disappointment. Starting on a second biscuit, a lightbulb came on in Eartha's head. It worked, though, didn't it?

Getting up, she stared out at the back garden, where flowers were waiting to be potted, and made a decision.

This year, she wouldn't bother with the front garden.

Of course, she couldn't waste such beautiful flowers, so they could go down the bottom of the back garden in pots beneath the tree she'd planted for Ghillie.

And while she was at it, she'd plant up a couple of tubs for Gloria to put on her patio.

Eartha sighed with pleasure. The front garden could do whatever it liked. From that moment on, she didn't care.

If the lawn burst out in multicoloured mushrooms and the world's biggest dandelions, it was OK with her.

Friends, she decided, were far more important.

*   *   *   *

"But you'll miss the competition," Eartha said as she stood in her front garden, chatting to Gloria some weeks later. "They'll be round to do the judging tomorrow."

"Yes, I know," Gloria said. "And I didn't really want to miss it, but I promised Graham I'd help him. I was wondering –"

She stopped to give Eartha a grin.

"Could you do it for me, Eartha? You know, when they come round? Could you stand by the gate in case they have any questions? I mean, I haven't actually done anything but, well, you know, after last year . . ."

Eartha stared around at Gloria's garden. It was a breathtaking display of doing absolutely nothing.

Shrubs were so heavy with blooms they could hardly hold up their heads, and her lawn looked superb. The two pots Eartha had given her were an explosion of colour.

Eartha decided she would never understand the finer points of gardening. Some people just had green fingers.

She glanced down at her own garden. The lawn was so full of weeds, with so many different types of leaf, one could barely see the grass.

There would be no need to answer questions on that, even if she'd bothered to enter.

"Of course," she said. "I'd be happy to, Gloria."

Gloria gave her a hug.

"You're an angel. I shouldn't be too long."

*   *   *   *

It came as no surprise when Gloria took gold once again for the best front garden. Eartha stood, answering any questions from the judges.

Not that they had many. It was like the scene in her mind.

"Have you seen this garden?" The judge gasped. "It's just wonderful."

"Don't think there's any doubt about this year," the other said. "This lady could teach us a thing or two."

And me, Eartha thought sadly.

With a sigh, she turned in through her own gate.

"Excuse me?"

Eartha turned again. The judge was signalling to her.

"Is this your garden?"

Dumbly, Eartha nodded.

"Yes."

With a flourish, the judge handed her a rosette.

"Best wildflower garden we've seen," he said.

"But . . . but I didn't enter."

The judge looked at his list.

"Number twenty-four? Eartha Bloom?"

She nodded.

"Congratulations," he said. "Good to see a natural garden. Vital for the wildlife. Well done."

Grasping the silk rosette, Eartha stared in amazement. How on earth? But in that second, she knew. Gloria had entered her in the competition.

Oh, bless her, Eartha thought, as she stepped indoors. What a lovely friend she is.

A sudden idea popped into her head. A cake. She'd bake Gloria a lovely cake to say thank you. And she'd ice it to match Gloria's garden.

Some time later, Eartha stared down at the finished cake.

An immaculate lawn and colourful flowers. A fitting tribute, if she said so herself.

The phone rang as she slipped the cake into a tin. It was Gloria.

"Hi, Eartha! Fancy a cuppa? I've got something to show you."

"I've got something to show you, too," Eartha said. "I'll bring it with me."

*   *   *   *

"There's no commitment," Gloria said. "But it's the last of the litter and well, you know me, Eartha. She's such a little darling, I ended up bringing her home with me.

"It's a bit presumptuous of me, I know, and please don't feel any obligation. I'm quite happy to keep her if you'd rather not. I do understand."

Eartha crouched down to stroke the little spaniel puppy.

"Graham's dog had a litter of six and Poppy here is the last one," Gloria said. "Isn't she gorgeous?"

Eartha picked up the puppy and cuddled her.

"I'd love her," she said.

"Oh, I'm so pleased!" Gloria cried. "I've missed our walks together." She glanced at Eartha's hands. "What happened to your hands?"

Eartha grinned.

"I forgot to wear gloves when I used the food colouring on your cake," she said. "But on the plus side, I've finally got green fingers." ■

Goldfinch

THIS small bird has colourful plumage, with a lovely red face, a white and black head, and a band of bright yellow on the wings. Their black tails have white flashes, too. With their delightful twittering call, it's little wonder that collectively they're known as a charm of goldfinches. Although they enjoy farmland, goldfinches can also be seen in our gardens.

The goldfinch feeds on dandelion seeds, while its slim beak ensures it can access its favourite thistle seeds. Due to the fact thistles have thorns, which are associated with Christ's crown, the goldfinch is also known as "saviour" bird. In Anglo-Saxon times it went by the name of thisteltuige or thistle-tweaker.

The breeding season begins in late April through to the end of July. They lay between three and seven eggs, which are pale blue speckled with brown, and usually nest high up in hedges or shrubs, or on the outer branches of trees. While they may return to the same nesting area, they build their nests afresh each time. ■

Forgive And Forget

by Barbara Dynes

THE invitation arrived by post, just as Jenny was about to leave the house. Glossy and gold-edged, it was from her sister, Donna, inviting her to her thirtieth birthday party.

Jenny stared at it. Did Donna really think she would go?

"No way!" she said aloud, throwing the invitation on to the table. Really flustered now, Jenny went out to her car.

Her morning had started off so well, too.

It was a Wednesday – her day off from managing the café – and the first Wednesday in the month, which made it book club day.

She'd been so looking forward to this coming meeting and a discussion about the club's latest read: a twisty whodunnit now tucked in her bag.

But today's post had upset all that.

Relax, Jenny, she told herself as she drove, taking deep breaths.

By the time she got to Susan's house, Jenny had forced that unwelcome invitation to the back of her mind.

She loved running this book group – they were all such lovely people and now really good friends.

Ten bookworms had registered at first, all very keen; they'd had to be to endure two hours on those hard seats in the church hall!

Now, with the hall unavailable, each member took a turn at playing host. Today, at Susan's, only three other people had shown up.

"Has everyone read the book?" Jenny began.

"Sorry, haven't had a minute! The kids have both had colds so it's been a nightmare," Poppy confessed. "Barry's doing overtime – we need a new fridge."

Jenny smiled. Poppy rarely finished a novel, anyway; she'd admitted using these meetings mainly as an enjoyable break from her family.

"And I've been trying to lay a patio all week!" Bob put in.

Great, Jenny thought, hoping that Susan and Grant had read at least

Illustration by Ruth Blair.

a few pages. She glanced around her.

Susan's lavender-scented lounge, with its pristine matching cushions and curtains and immaculate off-white carpet, could have emerged from the pages of a Jane Austen novel, she thought enviously.

Jenny pictured her own flat – piles of books, too many ornaments, far too much clutter. No excuse at all, seeing as she lived alone.

Now, amid the chaos at home, sat that unwelcome invitation.

Her insides did a somersault at the thought: she should have put it straight in the recycling . . . except she felt honour-bound to answer it.

One of those "Sorry, I cannot attend" cards, signed, would do the job.

Jenny tried to concentrate on the meeting.

"I loved the book," Susan was saying. "A really good detective story!"

"Agatha is miles better," Grant declared. "Her plots win hands down!"

Jenny smiled. She expected that from Grant, who was divorced and ran his own computer business.

A bit older than her – fortyish – he had a thing about Agatha Christie's books.

Jenny made a couple of comments on the novel, which she'd enjoyed, in the hope of getting a discussion going. But there was no real response.

Just as well, because her mind was elsewhere.

What was her sister thinking, sending her an invitation?

It was months since they'd last had contact, after that final awful row.

Had Mum still been alive, she'd have got them back together somehow, Jenny thought ruefully. Mum was expert at such things.

But she could see no way through.

A silence hovered in the lavender air.

Jenny looked at her book group. Ex-Marine Bob seemed to be half asleep, Poppy was staring at her phone, as usual, and Grant sat examining his finger nails.

Needing to wake them all up, Jenny opened her copy of the detective novel.

"In chapter fourteen, Sean forgives Katie at the drop of a hat," she declared loudly. "I thought that was most unlikely, didn't you?"

Everyone sat up, alert once more, thank goodness.

But Jenny frowned.

What an unfortunate scene to choose! About forgiveness . . .

Yet she'd picked this chapter for discussion ages ago, before that invitation came.

Maybe her subconscious was playing tricks? Waiting for a reaction, she closed the book too hard and her bright blue bookmark flew out.

It lay, conspicuously out of place, on the off-white carpet.

Grant retrieved it.

"I disagree. I thought that scene worked well," he answered, handing over the bookmark. Jenny smiled her thanks.

His gaze seemed to meet hers for a fraction too long, or was she imagining things?

Quickly looking down at her notebook, she began to doodle.

"I daresay, in the story, Sean was in love with Katie." Poppy sighed. She might rarely finish the novels, but she always had something to say. "Give me a happy ending, every time!"

"Poppy's right," Susan put in. "My husband refuses to remove his shoes when he comes in from the garden. But if you love the person . . ."

Blushing, she stood up and hurried out of the room, mumbling about coffee.

Jenny bit her lip, Susan's words going round and round in her head.

She loved Donna. Donna was her sister and she missed her terribly.

But when your sister "stole" your boyfriend . . .

As she doodled, Jenny allowed her thoughts to wander back to the day she'd met James at a friend's wedding.

He was funny and warm and they hit it off straight away. She really liked him and they soon began seeing each other.

Then, after a few dates, Jenny introduced James to her flirtatious, single sister. Talk about turning on the charm – Donna did that in spades! He fell for it and that, as they say, was that.

It didn't last – Donna and James split up soon after.

Donna now had a new guy, apparently, and she had sort of apologised – a scribbled line in her Christmas card.

Still angry and hurt, Jenny had ignored it, refusing to get in touch.

Now, she turned back to the meeting. Grant was speaking.

"If you don't forgive, you risk growing bitter and that's not good," he declared. "What do you think, Jenny?"

Jenny stopped her doodling and frowned at him.

"It depends on the situation, surely?" she said.

"Forgive and forget is my motto," Poppy chipped in. "Life's too short."

Grant cleared his throat.

"Changing the subject, I've only just got around to reading Daphne du Maurier's 'Rebecca' for the first time. Amazing!

"D'you reckon it could be our book choice soon?"

Everyone was really keen and Jenny, relieved to talk about something else, agreed to put it on the list.

"I'll have to go to the library," she said. "I loaned my copy to someone years ago and never saw it again."

"Well, I've a second copy – you're welcome to borrow that," Grant promised. "Look, after coffee, shall we wind this meeting up for today?

"By next time, we should all have finished the current book. OK?"

Jenny smiled at him gratefully.

*　*　*　*

When she got home, there it was, sitting on the table: the invitation. The elephant in the room.

Jenny picked it up. She'd been too shocked earlier to read the message properly.

Opposite the words: *We'd love to see you, Jenny. Love, Donna and Paul*, was another apology: *So sorry again about James. Donna.*

Jenny realised her phone was ringing. It was Grant.

"Hi! I've found that other 'Rebecca'. Just thought I'd tell you."

"Great! Could you bring it next time, please?"

"Sure! I'm sorry the meeting dipped like that, Jenny." He hesitated. "I could bring the book along to the Red Lion later, if you're not doing anything? Only it's my birthday!"

"Oh!" She grinned. So that was why Grant had rung, rather than e-mailed. Well, a chat would be rather nice.

*　*　*　*

The Red Lion was crowded. Jenny insisted on buying Grant a birthday drink and they found a corner table.

Then, triumphantly, he produced a well-thumbed paperback copy of "Rebecca".

"Someone loved this book!" Jenny laughed.

"I think it was Mum's. My wife wasn't a reader. But 'Rebecca' has the lot, don't you think? Wonderful characters, romance, mystery – "

"As good as Agatha's stuff?" she teased.

"Possibly not! Jenny, about this morning – I hope you didn't think I was implying that you were bitter? Far from it!

"Only you did seem a bit upset." He touched her arm. "Sorry, it's none of my business."

Jenny played with a beer mat.

"It is hard to forgive, sometimes." She took a deep breath, needing to talk. "My sister – well, no, you won't want to hear . . ."

"Go on, please."

"Well, OK . . ."

Jenny briefly filled him in about her rift with Donna.

"Now, I've been invited to her thirtieth birthday party, but I won't be going," she finished.

She sat back. It was such a relief to talk about it. Grant was staring into his glass.

"I felt the same when Joy left me for someone else."

"Of course you did –"

"But I was wrong! Our marriage was not working, I get it now."

Jenny frowned and Grant switched the conversation back to the book club.

She thought one of his suggestions, that now and again they could all read and comment on a short story rather than a novel, was a brilliant idea.

"Poppy might actually have time to read and enjoy it!" He smirked.

Later, as they left the pub, Grant turned to her.

"D'you reckon you and that guy, James, would have stayed together?"

"Probably not!" Jenny laughed. Having revealed the story to Grant, she felt better about it. She pulled a face. "He liked fishing and football!"

"Then let go, Jenny. Your sister needs a second chance: life's too short, as Poppy said." Once in his car, he leaned through the open window.

"Can we do this again?" he asked, smiling.

"I'd love to," Jenny said warmly, her heart beating faster. What a wonderful idea!

After Grant had driven away, she sat thinking. People dealt with life so differently.

There was Susan, forgiving her husband with his messy shoes and Grant, forgiving his wife for leaving him.

No comparison between the two situations, of course, yet each important in its own way.

So many stories – where did her own come, in the scheme of things?

Jenny started the car. Donna's favourite colour had always been green. A classy green top would make a good present for her thirtieth.

And some roses: red roses. They symbolised love, didn't they? ■

The Leaning Tower Of Books

by Susan Blackburn

HEARING a muffled curse and the sound of something toppling, I rushed into the lounge.

My husband Ian was kneeling on the floor, surrounded by books.

"Oops. I meant to move that pile somewhere else." I giggled.

But the giggle froze in my throat as, instead of the usual chuckling and a "you and your books", he gave me a look that would have frozen Niagara Falls.

"It's all getting a bit much, isn't it, Carrie?" he muttered as he swept out of the door.

As I looked around the room I could see his point. Books were in piles everywhere, because all of the many bookshelves we had in our tiny cottage were full.

I sighed.

OK, I was a bookaholic. I couldn't resist them.

I loved the wonderful aroma of new pages, the feel of an unbroken spine between my hands, the wonderment as I turned the pages.

My idea of heaven was entering a bookshop, breathing in the heady, unique scent and browsing the shelves until I found myself at the till with a pile of irresistible treasure in my arms.

But now it all turned to ashes as I looked around our

Illustration by Shutterstock.

sitting-room, seeing it through Ian's eyes.

But what had suddenly happened?

It wasn't as if he didn't know my passion. He had from the first day we'd met at school.

It had become a standing joke between us. Until now. I could feel tears tightening my throat. Ian had never looked at me like that.

"Sorry." He picked his way over the books scattered on the floor and held me tightly against him.

"It isn't you. I've had a lousy day at work and something snapped when I knocked over that pile of books.

"Er, Carrie, love, can I smell burning?"

I gave a shriek as I navigated the small room at top speed and just managed to rescue the bolognese.

Pouring us both a glass of wine, I spooned the fragrant, garlicky dish into two bowls.

We ate, but instead of clinking glasses and our usual easy chatter, he seemed a million miles away.

Snuggled up on the settee later, I took a deep breath.

"We're all right, aren't we?" I whispered.

Ian hugged me tight.

"'Course we are, Carrie. Love you to the moon and back."

Why wasn't I convinced?

I was even less convinced when Ian started spending any spare time he had in the shed at the bottom of the garden.

"Go away, Carrie!" he'd snap when I tried to peep inside. "Can't a man have a shed to himself now?"

"I suppose," I said doubtfully. "It's just you've never seemed to need one before."

"Well, I do now," he said. "It's good to have some 'me' time, for you as well as me."

"I don't really feel the need for 'me' time, Ian," I said sulkily. "I've always enjoyed 'you and me' time, actually. I thought you did, too."

"Sure I do, but I'm resurrecting my old hobby of painting. I always found that very relaxing and I can do that whilst you're reading. I need good light and lots of space to splosh about in."

That did it. The shed wasn't particularly light.

Also, although not small, it wasn't exactly cavern sized.

And he always put his earphones in and listened to music, leafing through a magazine or catching up on some work, whilst I was reading.

As for painting? I'd never heard him mention painting in all our time together.

Whatever Ian said, he wasn't happy.

I'd driven him away, I thought in despair.

For the first time, I didn't look at my leaning towers of books of all shapes, sizes and genres with unconditional love.

Tomorrow, I decided, anguished but determined, I'd make a start on having a sort-out. It was Friday, so I'd have the weekend as well.

I managed to finish work much earlier than usual the next afternoon.

As I turned into our road, with boxes I'd cadged ready for my clear-out filling the boot, I nearly drove up the kerb.

It wasn't just that Ian was home from work – something practically unheard of due to his busy schedule – but that he was also hugging a tall, willowy blonde.

He kissed her on both cheeks, waving her goodbye as she drove off.

"The swine!" I fumed.

I swung the car round and drove back the way I'd come, ending up at the local woods.

Tears I couldn't hold back any more overflowed as I trudged through the magnificent ancient trees, dressed now in their glorious autumn attire.

"My husband's having an affair," I chanted like a mantra as I wended my way deeper into the woods. And, I thought, suddenly outraged, I was prepared to clear out my beloved books for him!

I went home to my mother, who lived in the nearby village. She hooted with laughter when I told her.

"Ian? Don't be so ridiculous, Carrie."

I didn't know whether her reaction made me feel better or worse.

"He's a very attractive man," I said huffily.

"I know, darling, but Ian?" She cackled. "And he wasn't exactly in a passionate clinch, was he? Just a peck on the cheek, you said."

"Both cheeks," I retorted. "And we do have neighbours. Especially Nosy Nina over the road. He wouldn't risk it, would he?"

"Well, the neighbours would see her there, wouldn't they?" Mum said. "Oh, Carrie, talk to him. Darling, you two are soul mates.

"I could see it the first time you brought him home for supper when you were both sixteen."

Mum gave me a comforting hug.

"Can I stay?" I whimpered, feeling like a little girl again, secure in her loving arms. "Sort myself out?"

"Of course you can. I'm going to see your gran over the weekend. Why don't you come with me?"

Taking a deep breath, I called Ian.

"I called at Mum's," I explained. "She's going to see my gran this weekend and I think I'll go along."

"Oh, sweetheart, I'll miss you. Give your gran my love, won't you?

"Love you!" he finished.

I relaxed at this typically sweet response. Like Mum said, this was Ian we were talking about.

When I got home after a weekend of love and laughter with Mum and Gran, Ian wasn't there.

In fact, for a moment, I wondered if I'd got the right address.

The kitchen was pristine, as was the lounge. It took me a second to register what I was seeing.

The bookshelves were still full of books, but now they all stood tidily upright, rather than higgledy-piggledy. And I was able to see all of the freshly vacuumed carpet.

I let out a cry of pure anguish.

Where were all the leaning towers of my beloved books?

"Hi, darling," a voice behind me said. "You're home."

"But am I?" I whispered.

Ian chuckled.

"You are, my love. Come with me."

He led me into the back garden and down towards his man shed, now painted a gorgeous muted red, sporting a pink ribbon of a deeper hue strung across the door.

Ian handed me a pair of scissors.

"Cut it," he said excitedly.

Bemused, I cut the ribbon.

"Wait there," Ian commanded, pushing the door open a crack and sliding through.

Then he opened it wide, took hold of my hand and pulled me inside.

"Oh, Ian." I gasped.

The shed walls were lined with shelves upon which my books were stacked neatly. There was a wood-burning stove against the wall, and two cosy little fireside chairs either side of it.

On the opposite wall the window sported rose pink curtains, and underneath was a small antique table and chair.

"Welcome to 'The Book Shed'." Ian made quotes in the air. "Or whatever you decide to christen it."

"The Book Shed is perfect. But how? When . . ."

"Those times when I said I was constructing my man shed I was starting on this. I honestly have never minded your tottering towers of books, except for that one time it got to me.

"But when that happened, Carrie, it got me thinking. The cottage is tiny, but both of us love it and don't want to leave.

"What could be more perfect, I thought, than this shed as a library, a den for you to work or read in and have as many towers as you want."

"I certainly won't need them any more." I hugged my lovely man. "Look at the rest of the bookshelves just waiting to be filled!

"Oh, Ian, thank you so, so much. It's perfect – and so are you." I looked into his kind, understanding eyes, as I'd done every single day since I met him.

"You can't have done all this on your own, though?" I said.

"Chrissie, a colleague from work, helped me. You staying over at your mum's this weekend did us a favour, because luckily we were both free and able to get it all finished without you seeing anything."

"Is she a tall, willowy blonde?" I asked nonchalantly,

"I dunno," Ian said. "I suppose. Why?"

"Oh, nothing." I chuckled. "It's just that Nosy Nina from over the road sort of dropped hints that my husband seemed to be 'entertaining' . . ." it was my turn to do air quotes ". . . a tall, willowy blonde."

"Really? She thought . . ." Ian's face took on a smug expression. "Well, I am a very attractive man, after all."

"I'll drink to that," I said. ■

Rye, East Sussex

Mediaeval sailors familiar with Rye as one of the Cinque Ports might feel lost if they were to visit the town today. From enjoying a spot in a bay in the English Channel, where it was a busy fishing port, the town now lies two miles inland!

What happened? The change came about almost overnight when a great storm in 1287 reshaped the southern coastline. It brought massive quantities of gravel into the harbour. The storm also caused the River Rother to change course. Previously joining the sea at New Romney, 15 miles distant, it now found its outlet at Rye.

Our sailor might recognise some of the local hostelries, though. The cellars at the Mermaid Inn date back to 1156, though the inn itself was rebuilt after difficulty with French raiders in 1377 resulted in most of the town being burned to the ground. Hidden within, a secret passage allowed a quick getaway for notorious 18th-century smugglers the Hawkhurst Gang, if the excisemen came calling.

Smugglers risked the death penalty if they were caught. Today, Gibbet Marsh is the peaceful setting for the Rye Windmill on the River Tillingham. A windmill has stood on the site since the 16th century. The current mill, a Grade II listed building now run as a B&B, was built in 1932 after a fire destroyed an earlier mill.

The Little Shop Of Hope

by H. Johnson-Mack

SUMMER. It was one of those heavenly mornings of golden sun and glorious blue sky, when all seemed right with the world. Well, not quite all.

From the apartment window above her shop, Caro could see across the tree-lined Church Lane to the greystone St Gregory's where later would echo the sound of laughter and happy newlyweds.

Now, a young woman sat alone in the church's shadow. Her sorrow made Caro forget her own worries, hurry downstairs and approach.

"Are you here for the wedding? If so, you're early."

The girl swallowed.

"I'm not invited," she whispered.

It wrung Caro's heart. She held out a hand.

"You look like you could use a drink. My shop's just there; why don't you come and have a brew?"

Two coffees later, sitting side-by-side on the chaise-longue in the fashion corner of Pandora's Box, her kaleidoscopic store, Caro knew her guest's history of romance with the man about to marry someone else.

Penny was a part-time assistant curator. She was also half Caro's age, with a sweet face and unassuming manner.

"I shouldn't have come," she admitted. "It was silly."

"We've all done foolish things." Caro sighed. "Believe me, you'll laugh over this one day."

"It's easier to believe the bad stuff."

"Not in my world," Caro declared. "Now, how do you fancy helping me dress the shop window for a summer afternoon tea?"

Penny considered, then nodded.

"Sounds like fun."

In reality, she spent more time wandering round the shop exclaiming at all she found than dressing the window.

Caro was just happy to see a smile on her face.

Illustration by Sarah Holliday.

Besides, it was lovely to meet someone as enthusiastic about Pandora's Box as she was.

The cosy cream-and-beamed space crammed with curios and vintage fashion had been created from Caro's collecting over the years.

"I love this!" Penny posed before a bevelled mirror, a 1950s cartwheel hat perched on strawberry curls. "And ooh, an Art Deco shell bag! How did I not know about this shop?!"

Caro recalled the worrying letter she'd received from the bank.

"You're not the first to say that. We are off the beaten track, I guess." Penny frowned.

"You need to advertise better. Get Pandora's on the internet."

"I'm not great online. I don't suppose you'd be looking for extra work?" Caro ventured hopefully.

"A few more hours would come in handy," Penny admitted. "And there's definitely something about this place . . ."

"Then you're hired! Let's have another drink to celebrate."

Later, when the bells of St Gregory's signalled a marriage, Caro looked anxiously at her new assistant.

But Penny, creating Pandora's Facebook page, barely blinked.

*　　*　　*　　*

Autumn. Caro tucked her scarf tightly round her neck and moved a little faster as a sharp wind whipped down Church Lane.

Despite the chill, this was her favourite season; all blazing fires, smoky mists and bowls of comforting soup.

Penny welcomed today's selection from the corner café, exclaiming how hungry she was. Caro smiled.

Not only had Penny breathed new life into the business with her marketing ideas, she'd reminded the older woman of what the world looked like through twenty-something eyes.

Not that Caro was unhappy; far from it.

She loved her little shop, and living in this pretty, winding close. But after that bank letter with its warning of her loan extension being the last, Penny and her successful sales methods were an absolute godsend.

She was working on a new display when a man entered the shop.

"Euan!" Penny exclaimed, seeing him. "What are you doing here?"

"Looking for a present for Mum," he said, peering about him. "So, this is the famous Box."

When Penny remained unusually silent, Caro smiled.

"Welcome to Pandora's − Euan, was it?"

"This is the museum curator's son," Penny reluctantly explained.

"I thought Pandora's Box an unusual name for a shop, given what legend says it contained," Euan mused. "Now it makes more sense."

Caro laughed.

"I'll take that as a compliment, I think! We're all about memories here; reviving precious ones and making new.

"Penny, why don't you help Euan find a gift whilst I finish the window?"

Flushing, Penny guided Euan to the jewellery nook.

The young man eventually left with a smile and small package in hand. He'd chosen a delicate Victorian brooch, perfect for a curator.

"What?" Penny demanded.

"He likes you, Pen," Caro said with a smile.

"He's just a work colleague," Penny said, but a blush had begun to blossom on her cheek.

"Men don't look like that at 'just a colleague'. Well, it's the season for all things magic. Maybe we could brew a love potion for you . . ."

Penny laughed as Caro donned a dark conical hat. Then she sobered.

"He asked me to dinner," she admitted. "And he does seem nice. But after the Fraser disaster, I'm afraid history will repeat itself."

"Oh, love. You mustn't let one mismatch hold you back you from finding happiness. Remember Pandora's legend − though the evils of the world were locked in that box, hope was, too."

"So I should believe in happy-ever-afters?"

"Exactly. Or a little magic, at least. These hats look good, you know," Caro added. "We should wear them in the run-up to Hallowe'en, maybe have a 'Witchy Week' promotion."

"Great idea!" Penny agreed. "Bags I get the black flapper dress . . ."

* * * *

Winter. Caro leaned out of her apartment window to breathe in the crisp December air.

Dusk was falling, early as always in wintertime, and thanks to a heavy frost, Church Lane was kissed by crystals.

Pandora's Box and the flat above were festooned in festive greenery. A plump tree held pride of place in the shop window, with beaded purses, perfume bottles and seasonal accessories sparkling beneath.

Sales were going well, thanks to the pair's promotional efforts. Their New Year project was to improve these further by investing in a website.

Life had improved for Penny in other ways as well. Perhaps buoyed by the Hallowe'en compliments she'd received, she'd accepted a party invitation from Euan. They'd been going out ever since.

There was something extra special in the air this year, Caro mused happily on Christmas Eve as she shut the door behind a late customer for whom she'd gift-wrapped an old Paris scene snow globe.

Though not quite over, it had turned into a positive year for Caro and her little shop, and she was already looking forward to the new one.

Penny might not be with her quite as much now, but she was still Caro's good luck charm. She'd wrapped the beaded Indian shawl she'd chosen for Penny's Christmas gift with extra love and care.

After meeting her assistant for a quick drink and exchange of presents at the corner café, she was off to spend the next couple of days with her sweet if ailing Aunt Emma, who adored Caro's roast dinners, and also wanted to contribute to Pandora's vintage section after a huge clear-out.

Caro took a last look round before heading upstairs to pack a bag.

Her festive wish this year would be for her shop to be saved.

"Merry Christmas, little Box," she whispered as she drew the door closed. "I'll soon be home again . . ."

*　　*　　*　　*

Spring. Caro cleared away the Easter window display.

The season of awakening had been a little late in coming, but now the trees along the lane were wide awake and adorned in green, the tulips in the corner café tubs waving rainbows of plum and candy colours.

Caro's spirits were lifted still further when Penny unexpectedly arrived.

"You're not supposed to be working today! Is everything all right?"

But she could see from Penny's radiant expression that it was.

"I have some news," she said. "Euan and I . . . we're engaged!"

"Oh, love!" Caro squealed. "I'm so happy for you!"

"I feel as if I have you to thank," Penny said shyly. "There's something about you, and this shop, that works some kind of magic . . ."

Caro sighed.

"I feel the same about you. The day we met, I'd had a letter from the bank. Pandora's was in trouble, and if it hadn't been for you, I probably would have lost all this.

"Now, we're actually the right side of breaking even. You saved me, Pen."

Penny cast herself into Caro's arms.

"You saved me, too. You, and your little shop of hope!"

"We need a drink," Caro declared. "I'll put the kettle on.

"I'll get that," she added as the telephone rang.

"I'm sorry, Pen, I have to go," she said moments later, her happy bubble burst. "My aunt Emma is in trouble!"

* * * *

The sun had given way to showers when Caro returned home. Penny was still there, she noticed, easing her way into the shop.

"I was happy to help," Penny said when Caro thanked her for keeping Pandora's open. "Is your aunt OK?"

Caro sighed.

"Emma's moving into sheltered housing. She's been looking for some time and has found the perfect place, only it's smaller than her two-bed house so she doesn't have room for all her things."

As she spoke, she carefully unveiled the bundle she carried. Penny gasped in surprised delight when she saw a small black-and-tan terrier.

"She was a stray Emma took in," Caro explained as Penny fussed over the timid creature. "But the new home won't allow pets and . . ."

"So this little one has nowhere to live?"

Caro shook her head.

"Emma begged me to help. I think she wants me to adopt her."

"And will you?" Penny asked.

"With a face like that?" Caro smiled, lifting the dog. "No question."

* * * *

Summer. Caro sighed, tilting her face to the sun. The weather was perfect; cobalt sky scattered with scudding marshmallow clouds.

It was Penny and Euan's wedding day, and Caro was taking the opportunity to sit and reflect in the place she'd first met her.

How glad she was that she'd gone down that day!

In doing so, she'd not only discovered someone who loved Pandora's Box and helped save the shop. She'd also found a friend.

A wet nose nudged her hand and, looking down, Caro smiled.

She and her adopted stray were inseparable these days.

The little terrier was now as much a part of Church Lane and Pandora's as Caro herself.

"OK, enough wool-gathering," she said now to the dog. "It's time to get ready for Pen's big day."

I'm so lucky, she thought. I'm living my dream, I have fantastic friends and now a heart who loves me unconditionally. Penny was right; there was something magical about that little shop of hers . . .

"What's her name?" Penny had asked on that rainy day when Caro first brought the terrier home.

"She doesn't really have one," Caro explained. "Emma just called her 'pet'."

"Oh. What will you christen her, then?"

Caro looked round Pandora's Box, full of memories and second chances, then into the wide eyes peering up into hers.

"Hope," she said softly. "Her name is Hope." ■

Robin

WHILE we may intrinsically link the beautiful robin with wintertime, this little fellow can be seen year-round in hedgerows, woodlands and gardens here in the UK. With its red breast, it's also the easiest to identify.

The red plumage is a sign of an adult robin, both for males and females, with the latter laying around five to six pale blue eggs per brood. And, while they like to nest near the ground in hedgerows and hollows of tree roots, they are also great at improvising, finding unusual nesting spots in everything from old flower-pots to concealed nooks in farm machinery!

They enjoy eating insects and worms, seeds and fruits, and are particularly partial to mealworms. These birds are also very territorial and will chase off intruders.

We always associate robins with Christmastime. They first appeared on festive greetings cards in the Victorian era, with the red uniforms of postal workers thought to be the inspiration for this much-loved tradition. ∎

A Rose By Any Other Name

by Patsy Collins

DIANE returned from her few days away and surveyed the mess. She'd been assured everything was "hunky dory" and the new windows were in.

The second part probably was the case, but the workmen and their ugly scaffolding, white vans and loud radio were still there, so the house actually looked worse than it had before she'd left.

It's temporary, she reminded herself. They just needed to clear everything away and then she'd have her home and her peace back – and no more draughts come winter.

She avoided looking at her poor trampled garden as she carried her case down the path and left herself in.

"Everything OK?" she asked the man making tea in her kitchen.

She'd suggested they make use of it, guessing they'd be tempted to do so even without permission.

"Hunky dory, love, yeah," he said.

No surprise there, as he'd said it about the fact she'd be away for a few days, and that her driveway would be left clear, and almost everything else he'd expressed an opinion about.

She'd never heard his colleague say anything at all.

"Kettle's just boiled, shall I make you one?"

"I'll do it, thank you. I mustn't hold you up," Diane said.

He took the hint, and left with two mugs of very dark tea.

"We'll be done by lunchtime," he promised on his way out.

Diane kept herself busy unpacking, putting on a wash, inspecting the new windows from the inside, going through the accumulated post and making two rounds of tea for the workmen.

"Sorry, love, that spiky plant out the front is a goner," the window fitter said.

"The climbing rose?"

"That's what it was?"

And not just any climbing rose, but the one her beloved Gavin had bought her when they were on honeymoon.

Illustration by Ruth Blair.

He'd joked that he'd never promised her a rose garden, but they were going to start married life with their space filled with nothing else.

Diane hadn't minded that the space was no more than a two-feet-deep strip of the walkway outside their flat.

Most of that space had been filled with the mat outside their door, but there was just room for a plant pot.

Despite the shady and windy position, the rose did pretty well.

That was until they moved and it went into a larger pot and eventually into the ground outside her current home.

Once in good conditions, it was superb. In a very short space of time it had covered the trellis Gavin put up beside and over the front door.

For years it had bloomed reliably, producing masses of small, scented flowers in a delicate apricot shade.

She'd picked flowers every year on their anniversary.

She and Gavin had worn one each in their button holes when their son Max married.

Her granddaughters had collected the fallen petals to make magic potions, searched around the stems for Easter eggs, and helped hang fat balls for the birds from the sturdy stems in winter.

The rose had survived all this time. Perhaps it wasn't really dead?

The window fitter clearly knew nothing about plants.

Perhaps he just meant some of the top growth had snapped off? If so, it would soon regrow.

No such luck. Diane realised that when the scaffolding had been put up the plant was disturbed.

If she'd been told at the time she could probably have saved it, but the poor thing had been left with its roots exposed to the hot summer sun for over a week.

As it had been in full leaf and smothered with buds, it hadn't stood a chance.

To the workmen, it was just an accident. To Diane, it seemed to symbolise everything going wrong in her life.

Gavin hadn't been there to see its last two flowerings, but she'd thought she'd always have his roses to remind her of their happy marriage.

Their son's own relationship hadn't been so successful and he was now divorced. He saw his two girls, Mia and Avery, every other weekend.

Diane almost never did.

"Are you OK, love?" the fitter asked.

"Just give me a moment."

She went inside and shed a few tears, then pulled herself together.

It was an accident, and it had just been a plant.

She didn't need it to remember Gavin, and whether the roses bloomed or not, Mia and Avery wouldn't be there to collect the petals.

Diane wiped her eyes, blew her nose and went down to look at the windows from outside.

After a demonstration of the opening and locking of each she was able to reassure the fitter that, damaged garden aside, she was "hunky dory".

She signed for the work and waved them goodbye.

Max came to visit soon after.

"They've done a good job, Mum," he said of the windows.

"They look better, and with the cost of gas you'll soon get the money back in reduced heating bills."

He commiserated over the rose, but suggested buying another.

"I don't know the variety," Diane said, as if that was the problem.

It was true that Gavin had bought it unlabelled from a market stall, but someone would no doubt be able to identify it.

Surely such a pretty, long flowering, easy to propagate and trouble-free rose would still be offered for sale somewhere?

"Have you got a photo? If I post it online someone will tell me."

Diane produced a photograph and let him try.

When she and Gavin had gone anywhere which had roses growing or for sale, they'd looked to see if they could find one like theirs.

Although a few had been similar, they'd not been convinced they really were the same.

They could have tried harder, but it hadn't seemed important.

Now Diane felt that she would quite like to know, although not because she wanted to buy a replacement.

However identical the blooms and hips and leaves appeared, the plant

The Violinist

He seemed quite shy and diffident, this tousled-haired young man;
My friend sat so expectantly – I knew she was a fan!
He held his violin with love, caressed under his chin;
We waited in the sudden hush for his playing to begin.
And then those first few silver notes soared straight into my heart;
They pierced my soul with purity – a sweet and lovely dart!
He lifted us to dizzy heights, we crossed both time and space;
I looked around and saw such joy shine out from every face.
He held us all within his hands and oh, the time flew by;
It seemed we all expelled our breaths in one collective sigh!

Eileen Hay

wouldn't be her plant. And then there was replant disease.

"You can't plant a rose where one was growing before," she explained.

"It's something to do with them changing the soil. Putting something in or taking it out.

"The existing plant is fine, but a new rose will never get established in that spot."

"What about other plants?"

"They'll be . . . hunky dory." She might buy a clematis. That would look nice climbing up the now empty trellis.

Three days later Diane got a telephone call from Maureen, the mother of her former daughter-in-law.

They'd been friendly at one time, but hadn't spoken in a long while.

Diane couldn't recall when exactly, but it was certainly before the divorce had been finalised.

"Is everything OK? The girls?" Diane asked.

"Yes, absolutely fine. I'm calling about your lovely rose."

"It died," Diane said, trying to keep the tremble out of her voice.

"I thought as much when I heard you were trying to find out what it's called."

"You know it?" Diane guessed.

Maureen was as keen a gardener as she was and had admired the rose so much she'd begged for a cutting.

"No. I call mine Diane's rose and I'd forgotten that wasn't its proper name."

"It doesn't really matter," Diane said. "I'm pleased you got it to grow. Somehow, it makes me feel better to know it's surviving somewhere."

"Not just surviving, but thriving. Mine is now as big as yours was the last time I saw it and it's smothered in blooms."

"How lovely."

"I didn't call to gloat."

"I didn't think that!" Her comment about the rose had been genuine. She could have been jealous of Maureen still having her plant, and a husband, and getting to spend time with Mia and Avery, but none of Diane's losses were in any way Maureen's fault.

"I called to offer you a replacement. I struck a cutting a while back and it's doing well.

"It's plenty big enough to go in the ground now. Would you like it?"

"I would, very much."

"You can't plant it in the same place, of course."

"No, but I could plant it the other side of the door. Once it gets going I can train it over on to the trellis.

"It won't be exactly the same, but as close as it's possible to get."

"That's just what I was thinking. We could bring it over tomorrow?"

"Yes, please."

Diane had assumed that by "we" Maureen had meant herself and her husband.

"Granny!" Mia yelled, hurtling out of the car and into Diane's arms. Avery was right behind her.

The rose was almost an anti-climax after that, but together they got it planted and the girls gave it a good drink, carrying the large, heavy can between them and carefully trickling the water around the stem.

"It will need that much water every week," Maureen said.

"I don't know if Granny will be able to manage that great big can on her own, so I'd better bring you over to do it, don't you think?"

The solemnity with which the two girls promised to carry out the task made all three of their grandparents laugh.

"Their mother won't mind?" Diane asked.

"No. Actually, I grew the rose for her, but when she saw Max's post on the internet she said you should have it, and suggested I bring Mia and Avery to help you plant it.

"She even got a couple of books from the library to try to find the name."

"Will you please tell her that I've decided to name it Hunky Dory, and that she's given me the most wonderful gift." Diane beamed happily. ∎

Illustration by Mandy Murray.

A Major Problem

by Eirin Thompson

WHEN Gran went off to see her friend, Hazel, she asked me to come and look after her place while she was away.

"You can do what you like, as long as you remember two things for me.

"Number one, take in a parcel I'm expecting with parts for my knitting machine," she told me. "Number two, and more importantly, don't let anything happen to Major."

Major was Gran's cat. A spoilt feline who dined on roast chicken and smoked fish, he was the apple of her eye.

I was more sceptical.

It struck me that Major was a crafty so-and-so who could take up a whole sofa by stretching out languidly, and he had Gran wrapped round his little paw.

Still, I liked the prospect of living on my own for a day or two.

I got on well with Mum and Dad, but it would be nice to have a bit of space to myself.

"Since I'm working from home anyway, I'll just set up my laptop on your kitchen table, so it's no problem to listen out for your delivery," I told her. "And Major will be perfectly safe with me."

*　*　*　*

I drove Gran to the station to catch the train.

"Have a lovely time," I told her as I waved her off.

"Thanks, Cara," Gran replied.

I picked up some groceries and went back to make myself a nice lunch.

But in the kitchen, Major immediately started to cry.

"I'll feed you after I've had something to eat," I told him, slicing some cheese.

I tried to sit down with my rather lovely sandwich, but Major wouldn't let up with the meowing.

"All right," I conceded. "I'll feed you first and then I'll eat."

I looked through the various collection of tins and pouches that Gran had left for him.

"All the priciest brands, I see," I told him.

I scooped some lamb casserole cat food into his dish by the fridge.

He continued crying, refusing to touch a morsel.

"What is your problem?" I asked him.

Major went and stood by the place where I'd been cutting the cheese.

"You don't want cat food – you want cheese?" I asked him.

He began to purr.

"You're some cat," I remarked, then cut him a tiny chunk.

Once I'd finished, and Major had devoured both the cheese and the lamb casserole, I set up my laptop and got to work.

Major curled up on his blanket in his basket.

Five minutes later, the doorbell rang.

I saved my work and padded down the hall.

"Can you just sign here, please?" the delivery woman asked, handing me an electronic notepad.

"Certainly," I replied, setting Gran's parcel in the porch.

"Is this your little chap?" the woman continued.

Following her gaze, I found Major had slipped out past me and was sitting in Gran's flower-bed.

"I'm looking after him for my gran and I wasn't meant to let him out," I admitted. "I'd better try to pick him up before he goes any further."

I walked slowly towards Major, trying to make my voice soothing.

"Come on, little guy. Let's pick you up for a nice, big cuddle."

Major sat where he was until I was within centimetres of him – then he bounded off, over the wall and on to the footpath.

"Oh, Major!" I fumed.

"It looks like you're going to have a job getting that one back under lock and key," the delivery woman commented. "Sorry, I have to press on and leave you to it."

Before she could disappear, however, Major jumped up on to the bonnet of her van.

I made my way alongside him. Maybe I could just sweep him up in my arms.

Once again, I was thwarted.

As soon as I came close, Major leapt from the bonnet of the car on to the trunk of the tree just beside it, then scrambled up into the branches.

The delivery woman shook her head and drove away with a smile.

*   *   *   *

"Major! Come on down," I coaxed. "I'll get you some more cheese."

I could plainly see Major sitting high up in the branches, not looking remotely interested in climbing down to join me.

It was sorely tempting just to leave the stubborn little rascal up there on his own, with nothing to eat and no blanket – see how he liked that.

But what if he took it badly and didn't ever come back?

Then it looked like hope was in sight.

Major started picking his way through the branches and heading downwards.

He only got so far, though, and then he began climbing down a little, then retreating back up.

He did this four times before I realised what was wrong.

It had been all very well when the delivery van was there as a springboard, but now that it was gone, getting down the final stage was too daunting for him.

"Oh, Major!" I cried. "Don't tell me you're stuck!"

What should I do? I racked my brains, but anxiety was starting to fog my thinking.

Suddenly, I remembered that Gran had a kitchen step – perhaps if I brought that under the tree and stood on it I could reach the cat.

"Hang on. I'll be right back," I promised, then dashed into the house.

The step only raised me about a foot off the ground.

I held my arms up to Major and called him again, but he just meowed sadly and wouldn't even attempt to jump down to me.

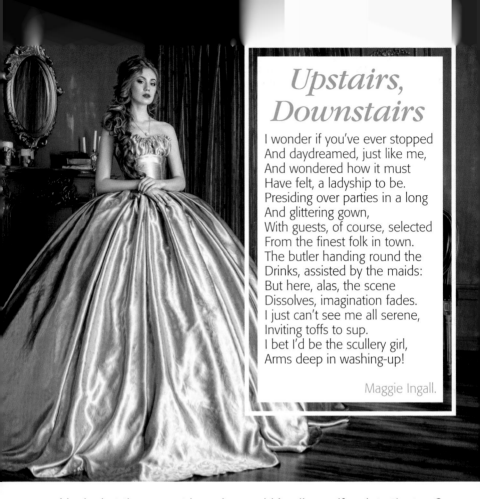

Upstairs, Downstairs

I wonder if you've ever stopped
And daydreamed, just like me,
And wondered how it must
Have felt, a ladyship to be.
Presiding over parties in a long
And glittering gown,
With guests, of course, selected
From the finest folk in town.
The butler handing round the
Drinks, assisted by the maids:
But here, alas, the scene
Dissolves, imagination fades.
I just can't see me all serene,
Inviting toffs to sup.
I bet I'd be the scullery girl,
Arms deep in washing-up!

Maggie Ingall.

I looked at the nearest branch – could I pull myself up into the tree?
It wouldn't be easy, but I should at least try.

One, two, three – disaster!

The kitchen step flew out from under me, but I managed to scramble my feet against the trunk and pull myself up with my arms, and there I was, sitting on the branch.

Oh! When I looked down, the ground seemed to be very far away and my head started to swim.

Don't look down, Cara, I told myself. Focus on Major.

I peered up to see where he'd got to, and he came weaving down to greet me.

"I couldn't leave you up here all by yourself," I told him, stroking between his ears. "You might have been frightened."

Then, just like that, Major turned around and, tail first, started reversing down the trunk.

In seconds he was on the ground and trotting up Gran's garden path.

"Why, you . . ." I began.

Now all I had to do was get down myself.

But I felt quite sick when I so much as looked at the drop.

I was stuck, I realised. I had no idea how to get down.

What could I do? I resolved to wait for a passer-by and ask for help. Exactly how they would assist me, I wasn't sure. Perhaps I was a case for the fire brigade.

It felt like hours, but it was only around five minutes before a man came by on the footpath.

"Excuse me," I called to him.

The man looked around, puzzled.

"I'm up here," I added.

He looked up.

"I wonder if you could help me," I began. "I seem to be stuck."

The man couldn't help smiling.

"Oh, dear. You've climbed this tree and now you can't get down. I see," he remarked.

"I was wondering if perhaps you could ring the fire brigade for me."

"The fire brigade?" He grinned. "You're sure about that? You're not all that high off the ground."

"You want to try looking at that from my perspective!" I snapped. "From where I'm sitting, it's a very great height."

"Are you frightened of heights?" the man asked.

"Not of heights, but of falling on to the footpath and breaking my neck, I am!" I replied.

"Well, hold on for a moment and I'll see what I can do," the man said. "I'm Corey. What's your name?"

"Cara. And, whatever your plan is, could you hurry up, please?"

Corey disappeared for a moment then reappeared with the most welcome sight – a ladder.

"If I prop it up against the tree and hold it, can you manage from there?" he asked.

"Of course," I replied.

But to climb down the ladder I needed to turn myself around on the branch.

When I tried, I found I couldn't.

"Oh, no!" I wailed. "I really am stuck! I'm too scared to move."

I thought Corey might get cross with me, but he didn't.

"Look, I'm going to have to fetch a neighbour to hold the ladder, and then I'll come up and get you," he explained.

"Can you be quick?" I wailed. "I'm starting to feel sick."

*   *   *   *

Corey held me firmly as he turned me on the branch and got my feet on to the nearest rung of the ladder, which Mr Featherstone was steadying at ground level.

He guided me every step of the way, and boy, was I glad to touch the footpath with my feet!

"I feel like I should be wrapping you in a foil blanket and giving you hot, sweet tea to drink," Corey joked. "What on earth made you feel like climbing a tree? Most people are done with that by the age of eleven."

"I didn't climb it for fun!" I protested. "My gran's cat ran up there and couldn't get down."

"So I need to fetch the cat now, too?" Corey asked.

"No – Major's long gone. He found his way down quite quickly once I was up there."

"Major?"

"That's his name – short for Major Tom, since he's a tom cat."

"In my experience, cats very rarely get stuck anywhere," Corey said. "They are accomplished escape artists."

"In your experience?" I queried.

"I'm a fire fighter, and we do sometimes get called out for cats stuck up trees, though rarely for their owners.

"The pets almost always get down themselves before we arrive on the scene, and then the families are terribly embarrassed."

I felt my cheeks redden.

"I'm terribly embarrassed," I admitted.

"I know. It's cute."

I didn't know how to respond to that, although I'd noticed that he was pretty cute himself.

"I have to find Major now, for Gran. I'm house-sitting for her."

"I don't suppose that's him on the window-sill?" Corey pointed.

"Oh, Major! There you are."

Before I could worry about him going off again, Corey had scooped him up.

I swiftly opened the front door and set Major inside.

When I explained to Corey how he'd got up the tree in the first place, by using the delivery van as a step, Cory nodded.

"It's a pity you didn't have a vehicle of your own – you could just have parked it under the tree."

Why couldn't I have thought of that and saved myself a great deal of embarrassment?

If Corey saw my blush as this dawned on me, he didn't mention it. Instead, he invited me out for a coffee.

"There's a nice place by the towpath, the Lock-keeper's Café," he suggested.

I'd already taken in Gran's delivery, and Major had had plenty of attention for a while.

I decided that I would tuck him up in his basket and leave him to it.

"Only if you let me buy the coffee to say thank you for getting me out of the tree," I countered.

Corey smiled.

"She's kind to animals and she doesn't forget a good turn. I knew this was my kind of girl."

"See you at three?" I asked.

"I don't see any 'major' problem with that," he replied. ■

Barn Owl

Shutterstock.

THESE beautiful nocturnal creatures are most likely to be spotted in the countryside or by rivers.

They really are quite something to see in the wild, with a wingspan of up to three feet.

And, if you're lucky enough to see one stationary, perched on a post, you'll see they are a sizeable 25 cm from head to talon.

Given their size, barn owls are surprisingly quiet in flight, and with excellent hearing and night vision they make great hunters. They prefer mice and voles, which they swallow whole.

As its name suggests, the barn owl loves to nest in barns, sheltered from the weather, or in tree hollows.

The female usually lays between four and six eggs, which all hatch at different times. The young are born without feathers.

With their heart-shaped faces, they are also referred to as "monkey-faced" owls, and there are thought to be around 4,000 pairs in the UK.

Barn owls usually mate for life and the males' colouring, unlike most bird species, is paler and more subtle than the female. ■

Damsons In Distress!

by Jane Bettany

I T was 24 hours since Alice Hardy had placed the large box of damsons outside her cottage.

She'd written a sign by hand: *Damsons in distress! Good homes needed – please help yourself.*

Despite the dubious attempt at humour, her offer of free fruit was clearly not tempting anyone. The tightly packed box was untouched.

Alice sighed. It was such a shame.

She hated the thought of good food going to waste.

The problem was, her garden boasted three of the fruit trees, and there was no way she could use it all herself.

She'd already made six jars of jam and three pies, which she'd frozen.

Alice had moved into Valley View Cottage at the end of April and started her job as a school administrator a week later.

Her new role was enjoyable, but exhausting.

Thankfully she only worked during term time, so the summer holidays were providing a welcome breathing space.

Leaving behind her cottage and the box of damsons, Alice walked down the hill, wondering why on earth she was on her way to a meeting of the village carnival committee.

She turned left at the cricket ground and past the church to the community hall, which was well used and large enough to accommodate most of the events organised by Belbrook residents.

The village offered unspoilt prettiness, as well as a pub, a café and a small post office.

The west side of Belbrook was dominated by a 1970s housing estate, but it was the quaint, older part of the village that had attracted Alice.

She'd viewed her tiny cottage soon after it came on the market and had put in an offer the same day.

As yet, she didn't know any of her neighbours, which was the real reason she now found herself heading into the community hall.

Illustration by André Leonard.

A recent edition of the village newsletter had appealed for volunteers to help with the annual carnival, and Alice knew it would be a good way to meet people and become part of the community.

The door to the main hall creaked as she pushed it open.

Inside, four people were gathered around a table.

Alice recognised Eileen Henderson, the proprietor of the village café.

When Eileen looked up, she seemed surprised by Alice's arrival.

"Am I late?" Alice asked, even though she knew she was a minute early. "I'm here to volunteer for the carnival committee."

"Hello," a grey-haired man with mischievous eyes replied. "I'm Ted Grainger, vice chairman of the committee and landlord of the Red Lion.

"You're not late. We started a few minutes early because we weren't expecting any new faces."

"We appeal for help every year, but no-one responds," a woman with short red hair added.

"I think people in Belbrook have an aversion to committees," a man of about her own age put in with a grin.

"Really, Daniel," Eileen admonished. "You'll put the young lady off before she's even sat down.

"Come in, dear. Find yourself a place at the table and tell us why you'd like to get involved."

Alice settled on one of the plastic chairs, feeling as though she were at a job interview.

"I moved to the village in April," she explained. "I thought this would be a good way to get to know people.

"I work as a school administrator, so I'm good with IT and PR. I know how to apply for funding, and I have experience of organising events."

Eileen's smile wavered a little.

"Well, thank you for joining us," she said. "Whatever your contribution, I'm sure it will be useful.

"As for the organisation of the event, we have that in hand. The carnival has been running for years and everything works like a well-oiled machine."

Ted harrumphed.

"Things may run smoothly, Eileen," he began, "but only because we've been doing things the same way every year. Don't you think it's time to do something different?"

Eileen frowned.

"If it ain't broke, don't fix it, that's what I always say."

"Like it or not, there are things that need fixing," Ted insisted. "Attendance figures were down last year."

Daniel nodded.

"I agree. The numbers were low, even though it was a sunny day."

"I conducted a brief survey at last year's event," the red-haired woman piped up. "Several people said they were getting tired of the old format."

Eileen drummed her fingernails on the table.

"You can't win them all, Penelope. There will always be people who are quick to criticise.

"In my experience, those people are usually far less willing to offer constructive suggestions for improvement."

A frisson of tension moved around the table.

What have I let myself in for, Alice thought.

"Perhaps our newest member has some ideas she'd like to put forward?" Ted suggested.

The committee turned to Alice expectantly.

"I've never been to Belbrook Carnival," she said. "It would help if you could tell me about last year's event."

She sat back and listened as the committee members outlined the previous year's running order.

"The carnival begins at the school, where a cavalcade of floats leaves at noon," Eileen began.

"The word cavalcade is an overstatement," Daniel pointed out. "There were only three floats last year, and none of them were impressive."

As the committee's description of Belbrook Carnival continued, Alice realised it could have applied to hundreds of events across the country.

There was mention of a tombola, splat-the-rat, jumble and craft stalls, a brass band, cream teas, inflatables and food vans.

"It sounds as though there's plenty to choose from," Alice remarked. "The only thing missing seems to be produce displays.

"They're very popular, especially if you offer prizes for the best cakes, preserves, vegetables, flowers and so on."

Eileen nodded.

"I like that idea," she said. "People love a bit of healthy competition. "We'd need a judge, of course. I suppose that's something I could do."

"You do realise that if you're the judge you won't be able to enter any of the competitions?" Ted pointed out.

Eileen steepled her fingers and smiled.

"Good point. In that case, Ted, you can do the judging. I know how much you enjoy a bit of cake and jam."

"I do have one more idea," Alice ventured. "How about making the event more of a celebration of community life?

"You could introduce a theme, and encourage people to come along in fancy dress. We could offer a prize for best costume."

Daniel gave her a thumbs-up, but Eileen pursed her lips.

"That's a lovely idea," she said, "but what would this theme be?"

Alice shrugged.

"I'm not sure."

"Why don't we go away and think about it?" Penelope suggested. "We could reconvene next week with our ideas."

"OK," Eileen replied. "Put your thinking caps on, everyone."

*   *   *   *

A robin was singing beautifully as Alice began her walk home.

As she neared the cricket ground, Daniel caught up with her and fell into step beside her.

"You live in one of the cottages on Brook Lane, don't you?" he asked.

"That's right," she replied. "Valley View Cottage. The one at the end."

"My grandparents live further along the row," he said. "I'm heading there now. Do you mind if I walk with you?"

"Not at all." Alice smiled. "On the way you can give me the low-down on the village. Have you lived here long?"

Daniel nodded.

"All my life, apart from three years at university." Daniel smiled.

"This is me," Alice said as they approached her house.

Pointing to the box of damsons, she added, "Please, take some fruit."

"I'll give you ten out of ten for the witty signage." Daniel laughed. "But you'll struggle to give damsons away in Belbrook."

"Why's that?"

"Every house in this part of the village has at least one damson tree in its garden." He grinned.

"Oh!" Alice exclaimed. "I didn't realise."

"These were originally workers' cottages for the stocking industry," Daniel told her. "Damson skins were used to make dye for the stockings, which is why there are so many of the trees around here."

"I'd love to find out more about the history of the village," Alice replied. "Maybe we could use damsons as the theme for the carnival."

"If you're interested, you should speak to my grandparents," Daniel suggested. "Come up to their house with me and I'll introduce you."

*   *   *   *

Alice arrived at the community hall the following Thursday reflecting on how much had changed in a week.

Seven days ago she'd hardly known a soul in Belbrook.

Now, she'd made friends with Daniel and his grandparents, and they'd also introduced her to several other Brook Lane residents.

She and Daniel had joined forces on a proposal for the carnival.

They'd met twice during the week to thrash out their idea, working creatively to put together a strong case for a damson-themed event.

Inside the community hall, Eileen called the meeting to order.

"The main item on tonight's agenda is the theme for our carnival," she said. "Does anyone have an idea they'd like to put forward?"

"Alice and I have been working on something," Daniel said. "We've typed up a proposal and we'd be happy to talk you through it."

Alice handed round the copies she and Daniel had printed out.

"As a newcomer to the village, I've been learning about its history," Alice began. "I discovered that, until the 1920s, residents celebrated the end of summer and beginning of autumn on a Sunday in September.

"It was known as Damson Sunday."

She turned to Daniel.

"As you know," he continued, "damsons played an important part in the village stocking-making industry, which is why there are so many damson trees around here.

"Traditionally, on Damson Sunday, people would gather together in the village square to eat damson pies, drink damson wine, play games and sing songs."

"Daniel and I are proposing that the carnival be moved to the third Sunday in September," Alice finished. "Damson Sunday."

Ted and Penelope were nodding, but Eileen remained tight-lipped.

"It would allow us to celebrate the distinct heritage of our village," Daniel continued. "It would encourage people to make use of their damson crop, instead of letting the fruit go to waste."

"Our plan is to promote the event to attract new visitors to the village," Alice added. "The aim is to raise funds for the community hall and bring extra trade to the pub, café and the shop."

Eileen sat up, her eyes suddenly bright and alert.

"Tell us more," she prompted.

"We thought you could offer damson cakes, pies and tarts in the café," Alice explained, "and cream teas served with scones and damson jam.

"At the pub, Ted, we thought you might be able to serve a special brew of damson porter and damson gin.

"There would be stalls and games, but also prizes for the best damson costume, and for jams, cakes and wine – all made with damsons."

"And chutney!" Eileen interjected. "Everyone loves my delicious damson chutney. I make it every year."

Alice smiled. She and Daniel had tailored their proposal to appeal to Eileen's competitive spirit, as well as her keen sense of good business.

"I think it sounds a tremendous idea," Penelope remarked. "A true celebration of damsons!"

"I agree." Ted nodded. "Especially if it encourages visitors from outside the village. That could be good news for my pub in the long term."

Everyone turned to Eileen, waiting anxiously for her verdict.

She was already outnumbered, and they could outvote her if necessary, but it would be good to have her on side.

"So, Eileen," Daniel began. "What do you think?"

"I think . . ." She tapped her copy of the proposal on the table in front of her. "I think it's a splendid idea.

"Of course, with my catering know-how, I'm best placed to lead on the organisational side of things. It will be hard work, but if you're all willing to chip in, I think we can pull it off.

"I suspect the residents of Belbrook would welcome a change from the usual carnival format. As I always say, a change is as good as a rest."

"What happened to 'if it ain't broke, don't fix it'?" Daniel whispered.

"I don't know," Alice muttered. "I'm just pleased Eileen likes our idea."

"Unless anyone else wishes to put forward an alternative proposal, I suggest we take a vote on the Damson Sunday idea," Eileen announced.

✳   ✳   ✳   ✳

Damson Sunday was a mild and beautiful day.

Late summer sunshine gilded the pub and café, and the crowded village square was adorned with bunting and damson-coloured balloons.

Hundreds of villagers had turned out for the event, several of whom Alice now knew by name.

There were also plenty of visitors from further afield.

The event had taken a lot of organising, and Alice and Daniel had met several times over the last few weeks.

Alice had told the local radio station about the event, and they had sent along their mobile broadcasting unit.

A reporter was interviewing Eileen.

She was attired in a damson-coloured dress and wide-brimmed hat.

As Alice and Daniel strolled past, munching mini damson tarts, they listened in to the interview.

"I run the café here in Belbrook," they heard Eileen say, "and I'm also chair of the carnival committee."

"And whose idea was it to bring back Damson Sunday?" the reporter asked.

Eileen twirled a hand in the air.

"Oh, it was very much a joint decision," she said. "The committee members felt the old-style carnival had run its course, which is why we made some changes. Based on the number of people here today, I think that was the right decision."

"Can you believe it?" Daniel laughed. "She didn't give us one ounce of credit for the idea."

Alice linked her arm through his.

"It doesn't matter," she said. "I'm chuffed everything worked out."

"Is that why you have an enormous grin on your face?"

Alice chuckled.

"No, that's because I've just been to the produce marquee. You remember that recipe for damson chutney your grandma gave me?"

"I do," Daniel replied. "And very good chutney it is."

"I thought so, too, which is why I entered a jar into the show. Eileen doesn't know it yet, but the results are in."

"And have you won first prize?"

"No, your grandma did," Alice replied, "but my chutney has been awarded the runner-up rosette."

"Yay!" Daniel raised his hand for a high-five. "I wonder how Eileen will take the news?"

Slapping the palm of his hand, Alice laughed.

"I'm sure she'll be magnanimous in defeat. What was it she said? There's nothing like a bit of healthy competition."

"No doubt she'll spend the next twelve months perfecting her recipe, ready for next year's event," Daniel remarked.

"You think we'll celebrate Damson Sunday next year?" Alice asked.

"I hope so," he replied. "And if it is going to be an annual fixture, I think you and I should continue to meet regularly – to keep the creative ideas flowing."

They had reached a stall selling damson ice-cream. Alice stopped and looked up into Daniel's eyes.

"Is that an excuse to keep seeing me?" she asked. "If so, wouldn't it be easier just to go out on a date?"

"Really?" Daniel smiled bashfully. "You'd go out with me?"

"I would if you asked me."

Grinning happily, Daniel took hold of her hand.

"Would you like to go out for a meal tomorrow night, Alice?"

"That would be lovely," she replied. "On one condition."

"What's that?"

"That we go somewhere that has absolutely no damsons on the menu."

"It's a deal!" Daniel laughed. "In the meantime, can I interest you in a damson ice-cream?" ∎

Chaffinch

THEIR collective name is a charm of chaffinches, or a trembling. They particularly love woodland and farmland, but chaffinches are commonly spotted in gardens, too, though are quite shy by nature. You can listen out for their cheerful trill song, and they have a variety of calls for defending territory or trying to attract a mate.

The males' plumage is orange-brown with a blue-grey cap, with wings of black with white flashes.

The females are duller in colour. Their plumage helps camouflage them when they are foraging on the ground for insects.

They are partial to caterpillars, spiders, seeds and berries.

A pair will both look after the young, with around four eggs laid in a nest usually constructed in the fork of a tree or in a shrub.

They line their nests with moss, feathers and wool for comfort.

The chaffinch is an adaptable bird and is widespread throughout the UK. ■

Seal Of Approval

by Alyson Hilbourne

"**H**ARRY, do you want to come ice-skating on Saturday?"

"Yeah, maybe. I'll ask Mum," Harry replied.

"He won't be able to go," Tom jeered. "He'll be out with his hippy mum, saving the planet on Saturday."

Harry's face burned. He clenched his teeth in an effort to keep from showing his feelings.

It was true. Mum was unlikely to let him go, but he'd ask.

He never got to hang out at the park or do the things the other kids did because Mum always had something better for them to do.

He was fed up with Tom and Jamie laughing at his mother for her jangly bracelets, scarves and sandals.

He wished she looked more like the other mothers at the school gate.

"We go to the beach on Saturday with the clean-up crew," Mum reminded him when he brought it up.

"It's much healthier than being inside and you enjoy it."

Harry wasn't sure he did.

Maybe he had when he was younger, when he could play in the shallows and chase seagulls, but now Mum gave him a sack and expected him to collect as much rubbish as she did.

They walked along the tideline collecting plastic bottles, crisp packets, toothbrushes and old lighters, then they moved on to clean the rocks.

The clean-up crew piled all the sacks together at the end of the day and congratulated each other on their good work.

Then they had tea from flasks and shared homemade biscuits before the sacks were taken in Dan's truck to the dump.

The next weekend they did it all again. There was an endless amount of rubbish to clear up on the beaches.

On Saturday morning, Harry unhappily accompanied his mum.

He dragged his feet along the sand, making tracks as he walked.

Illustration by Shutterstock.

A few hardy visitors huddled in groups as they tried to enjoy themselves. A couple of paddle-boarders in wet suits braved the sea.

Seagulls swooped and hovered over the white-capped waves.

Harry didn't feel like talking.

He was angry with Mum for insisting he came.

He tried not to think about the fun Jamie and Tom would be having. For once, he'd like to go out with his friends at the weekend.

Soon Harry had left the others behind and reached the rocks at the far end of the beach.

He had to fill the bag or Mum would give him her speech about saving the planet and the sea being the lungs of the world.

Then she'd look at him with sad eyes, showing her disappointment that he hadn't done more to help.

Harry was so wrapped up in his own thoughts that he almost missed it.

Between the rocks, mewing gently, lay a white furry body with huge brown eyes, a dark nose and black whiskers.

It was tangled in old fishing gear.

Harry stared.

The brown eyes stared back.

The animal tried to lift its head, but it was weak.

Tea Set

The tea set features on display
Its pattern known by heart.
My great-grandmother's wedding set
Complete in every part
With gentle hues and florals,
Motifs so sweet and fine.
I think of all the teatimes
That this set saw time to shine.
And fondly I remember
Being small and having tea
With sandwiches and treats and cakes
And the family there with me.

Judy Jarvie

It made a tiny noise.

Harry knew it was asking for help.

"Mum!"

He turned and yelled as loud as he could, but his words were ripped away by the wind.

He waved frantically, but Mum was staring at the tideline as she worked her way along.

In the end, Harry dropped his sack, put a rock on top to mark the spot, and ran as fast as he could back to his mother.

At last she looked up, an expression of alarm on her face.

Harry beckoned to her and she hurried over to him.

"Mum, I've found something."

He dragged her back to the rocks, finding the spot again by the bag he'd left.

"Look!"

"Oh, a seal pup!" Mum exclaimed.

"Good job, Harry. We'll get the RSPCA out. Can you go and fetch Christine?"

Harry ran off to find the beach clean-up organiser, while Mum scrambled in her pocket for her phone.

By the time the RSPCA arrived a small crowd had gathered to see the seal pup, but Harry knew the brown eyes were focused on him.

"A grey seal," the man from the RSCPA remarked. "Probably only a couple of weeks old.

"We'll get it to the sanctuary up the coast. They'll give it the best chance of survival."

"Can we go, Mum? It's my seal," Harry declared.

"You can follow the van," the RSPCA man replied. "I can't guarantee they'll let you in."

The man put on thick gloves and gently lifted the pup into a crate.

"They can give a nasty nip," he said. "We get several each year tangled up in stuff on the beach. You clean-up people are doing a fantastic job."

Harry stood straighter and felt a glow of pride.

Mum smiled at him.

They followed the RSPCA van in Mum's old car until they came to the sanctuary.

"You can watch through the glass," a smiling lady told them.

"We'll get this fishing rope off and check it over, then give it some food and put it in a pen for the night.

"If it's OK, it can go with the other pups.

"We have to keep them here over the winter and they'll be released in the spring."

Harry watched as the ropes were carefully cut away.

Then they felt the pup all over, listening to its heart with a stethoscope and looking in its mouth and its eyes.

When they'd finished, the lady came back outside to Harry and his mum.

"It's hungry, but I think with some feeding it'll be fine and we'll be able to release it into the wild again.

"If you hadn't found it, it would have died of starvation."

"Can I come and see it again?" Harry asked.

"If you like," the lady agreed. "We can always do with volunteers."

*   *   *   *

The following week couldn't go fast enough for Harry.

He barely listened on Monday morning as Tom and Jamie bragged about ice-skating and how good they had become.

On Tuesday, he went to the library and dragged out all the wildlife books he could find with information about seals.

On Thursday, the teacher told him off for daydreaming when he should have been doing a multiplication exercise.

He wanted to get back to the beach, to smell the salt, feel the sand and hear the waves.

He wondered if the seal pup felt the same.

The following Saturday, Mum drove him up to the seal sanctuary.

"You can't go in the pens because they need to be kept quarantined," the lady told them.

"But we need someone to help wash out the individual stalls where we keep the new arrivals."

Harry turned to his mother, his eyes wide with the question.

"You can stay if you want. I'll go to the beach and be back in a couple of hours." Mum smiled.

Harry worked with Tony, scrubbing out the small ponds in each stall. They wore rubber gloves, wellington boots and overalls.

It was a smelly job.

Afterwards, they walked past the cages and Tony explained about the animals they had in.

"Look, there are several pups like the one you found.

"Usually its best to leave them with their mother, but sometimes the mother leaves them.

"We have older seals, too. Some get tangled in ghost fishing gear or get hit by boats, and some ingest plastic.

"You've done a grand job helping today."

After that Harry went to the sanctuary every weekend during the winter.

He came to recognise the different seals and he watched his pup grow stronger and begin swimming in the large tank.

When it was time to release those that were well enough, Harry went with Mum to the beach.

The sanctuary staff carried the crates with the seals along the beach away from any people.

"So no-one will disturb them," Tony explained.

The doors were lifted on the crates and everybody stood back.

Harry's heart was in his mouth as he watched his seal slide out of the crate and work its way down to the water's edge.

It was no longer white and fluffy, but a mottled grey and brown colour.

It jumped awkwardly down the beach on its flippers, but when it reached the water it slipped easily away beneath the waves.

Harry let out the breath he hadn't known he was holding.

Then a small head bobbed up between the waves and two large brown eyes stared at Harry for a moment before the seal dipped below the surface and disappeared.

The seal was saying thank you, Harry was sure.

This was better than the park or ice-skating.

Harry turned away so no-one could see the tears in his eyes.

"Come on, Mum," he said. "We have a beach to clean up." ■

Dolbadarn Castle, Llanberis, Gwynedd

Situated within Eryri National Park (Snowdonia), Dolbadarn Castle, at the base of the Llanberis Pass, might look familiar.

It's been a favourite of landscape artists for centuries. J.M.W. Turner's atmospheric view of the castle was the painting that saw him elected to the Royal Academy in 1802.

It was built by Llywelyn Fawr (Llywelyn the Great), King of Gwynedd, in the late 12th century. In 1284, Edward I's armies captured Dolbadarn and dismantled it in part, pilfering timbers to use in the construction of Edward's new castle at Caernarfon.

The area is steeped in Arthurian myth. Legend has it that the sword itself rests in one of the local lakes: Llydaw, perhaps, or Dinas, or maybe Ogwen – no-one knows for sure. They're all handy for the nearby caves believed to be magical dormitories for King Arthur and his knights. Suspended in enchanted sleep, Camelot's heroes are said to lie hidden within, awaiting the call to come to the country's aid at a time of great peril.

A Little Knowledge

by Gwen Rollinson

I'M sure there was," I argued.

"Well, I'm not so sure, Jo," Mum replied, shaking her head.

"Which one had the striped head, then?" Dad asked.

"Oh, Terry, that was Bill Badger," Mum said exasperatedly.

The argument had been in full swing for over half an hour now, and we were still no nearer to resolving the issue.

"I think he had an orange-checked top," I put in.

"Rupert had checked trousers," Dad proffered.

"What's that got to do with anything?" Mum demanded.

"One of them had orange trousers," Dad continued, scowling at Mum.

"I think that was Pong Ping," Mum replied, returning the scowl.

"Who was Pong Ping?"

"Never mind who Pong Ping was!" I exclaimed. "We are trying to establish whether or not there was a pug in the stories."

"There's only one way to settle this," Dad said. "Put the kettle on."

He marched out of the room.

"I don't think that drinking more tea is going to help," Mum grumbled, but she switched the kettle on anyway.

We heard the scraping sound of the loft ladder being pulled down.

Mum and I grinned at each other.

I bet there's no other family in the world who could boast of arguing about Rupert Bear's friends at one o'clock in the morning!

Fortunately it was Sunday, so none of us had to be up for work or college, although I had agreed to meet up with Suzie and Declan at 10 a.m. to do a bit more facts cramming and discuss tactics for the upcoming Starmouth College of Further Education Annual Quiz.

I was determined we were going to beat Janice Woodford's team.

As Mum poured fresh tea into our mugs, Dad reappeared with a stack of old Rupert Bear annuals, which he divided up between us.

Quarter of an hour later, it emerged that I was right: there definitely

Set in 1980

Illustration by Philip Crabb.

was a pug in the Rupert Bear stories – named Algy – but that the character I thought was the pug, was, in fact, Gregory the Guinea Pig.

"You will be well set up if a question comes up on Rupert Bear at the quiz night." Dad laughed as we eventually said our goodnights.

* * * *

"Did you do anything last night?" Suzie asked as we waited for Declan.

"Not really." There was no way I was going to reveal the eccentricities of my family – not even to my close friend.

"I know," she said. "Saturday nights have never really been the same since 'Starsky And Hutch' finished."

Suzie was obsessed with the American TV cop show.

She had posters of David Soul and Paul Michael Glaser plastered all over her bedroom walls and a scrapbook full of articles about them.

"So what are our particular strengths?" Declan asked when we were eventually all ensconced in Suzie's parents' lounge with mugs of tea, a stack of biscuits and an even bigger stack of books.

"Well, if there's a set of questions on the life and career of David Soul, I reckon we'll do pretty well." I nudged Suzie. "And I've recently become an expert on Rupert Bear characters."

"What?"

"Don't ask, Declan," I replied, before he could pursue it.

"I'm fairly good on geography and world currencies," Declan declared. "As well as engineering."

Declan was training to be an engineer at Starmouth College, whilst Suzie and I were both doing a secretarial and office management course.

"Pop songs and sport are probably mine," Suzie added.

"I suppose literature and natural sciences are my best bet," I put in. I could list a fair number of capital cities, too.

"So if those topics are fairly well covered, we need to gen up on history, current affairs and that sort of thing," Declan said.

"I think 'The Guinness Book Of Records' would be a good one to look at, too," Suzie said, pulling out another of Declan's Christmas presents.

"Let's really go for it this year," Declan enthused. "After all, it's our last chance, as we'll be finishing our courses shortly afterwards."

I felt a stab of angst in the pit of my stomach.

I suddenly realised that we would no longer be having these regular sessions at Suzie's, and I wouldn't see Declan any more.

But now was not the time to be thinking of anything other than the quiz. I had Janice Woodford still to beat, and beat her I would.

We had been rivals ever since high school, when we both fancied the same lad, even though he went out with someone else in the end.

She beat our team last year and couldn't smile widely enough.

Fortunately, as she was doing the beauty therapy course, our paths didn't cross too often.

*   *   *   *

"Dad's picked up a couple of quiz books from the market," Mum said when I returned from the swimming baths the following Saturday afternoon.

"He thought it might help you to have a quiz night tonight."

"After 'The Two Ronnies'," Dad added. "The new series starts tonight."

Everything stopped for "The Two Ronnies" in our house – well, that and "The Muppet Show"!

*   *   *   *

"So far that's thirty-six points to Jo and thirty-one to you, Eileen. Let's proceed to the next round."

Dad was clearly relishing his role as quiz-master, and I had to admit that Mum and I were enjoying a bit of friendly competition, too.

"Anyone for drinking chocolate?" Mum asked after Dad announced the final scores. "Well done, Jo. You'll easily win the college quiz if tonight's anything to go by."

I beat Mum by 12 points in the end, but only because the final category was on national flags, which I had been genning up on.

"I'm still not convinced it was Stewart Granger in that film, though," Mum remarked as she heated up some milk in a saucepan. "I thought it was the one with black hair. What on earth was his name?"

"Most chaps had black hair before we had the colour telly," Dad pointed out.

"The letter C keeps coming to mind," Mum continued. "Or is it G?"

"Clark Gable?" I suggested.

"No, not him. He was in 'Gone With The Wind'."

"I think you're thinking of Cary Grant," Dad said.

"No," Mum replied. "It was Clark Gable in 'Gone With The Wind'."

"I mean that you are mixing up Cary Grant with Stewart Granger," Dad said in frustration.

"Oh, I see! Yes, you're right. I think they're similar. Both handsome."

"I know I always get them mixed up," I teased.

"Anyway, I thought Cary Grant was the one in that film," Mum explained.

"The answers at the back of the quiz book can't be wrong," Dad returned. "It clearly says Stewart Granger."

"It could be a misprint," Mum argued.

Unfortunately, this couldn't be resolved by a visit to the loft.

As many books as we had in our house, I was pretty sure we didn't have any on Hollywood film stars.

* * * *

"How did everyone get on with their additional topics this week?" Declan asked when we were back at Suzie's on Sunday morning.

"Very well," Suzie and I both answered in unison.

"Did everyone manage to watch 'University Challenge'?" he added.

"I managed to get one answer right," I replied proudly.

"That's one more than I managed," Suzie put in glumly.

"Well, the questions do tend to be a bit obscure," Declan consoled us.

I suspected he actually managed to answer a fair few, but modesty prevented him from saying how many.

I really would miss the three of us getting together when this was over.

Declan hadn't made any indication that he liked me, so the best thing I could do was focus on the quiz and forget about him as anything other than a team member.

I didn't want another Janice Woodford scenario arising with Suzie.

* * * *

The following Sunday, Declan and Suzie came round to our house as Suzie had relatives staying at theirs.

"What a lot of books!" Declan exclaimed as he entered the lounge. "I probably didn't need to bring any with me."

For some reason I felt slightly self-conscious, but at least this was one of the tidier rooms in the house, where books were housed neatly on bookcases without additional piles scattered about.

"It's brilliant," Declan added. "We've hardly any in our house. It's mainly what I've borrowed from the library."

"Really?" I felt a bubble of joy spring up inside.

"No wonder you're so knowledgeable," he added.

I'd never thought of myself as knowledgeable, but I supposed it was inevitable that I would have amassed a fair amount of information just by flicking through various books over the years.

"There's one here on the solar system." Declan picked it off the shelf and began to flick through its pages.

"Feel free to come over and borrow them any time," Mum said, carrying a tray of tea and biscuits into the room.

"Thanks, Mrs Turner. I will." Declan beamed at me, and I felt that bubble of joy bounce back up again.

Good old Mum!

"We're only a couple of weeks away from the big night," Suzie said when Mum had gone, and I had to force my mind back to the task in hand. "Are we ready?"

"Yes, we are!" we all chimed in.

I doubted that other teams had put quite as much effort into the quiz as we had, but then not everyone had Janice Woodford as an incentive.

"You wouldn't happen to know who the male star was in the 1955 film 'Footsteps In The Fog', would you?" Mum asked as Suzie and Declan were about to leave.

"That was Stewart Granger," Declan piped up. "My gran likes him. She wrote a letter to him once and he sent her his autograph.

"She showed me his letter. He said he'd just finished filming 'Footsteps In The Fog'."

His gran? It emphasised just how much older my mum and dad were compared to a lot of my friends' parents.

I'd bet that there wasn't a huge age gap between his gran and my dad.

"So that's sorted that one. Misprint, indeed," Dad remarked, catching the tail-end of the conversation.

He and Mum looked at each other and grinned, and it was lovely to see that spark between them.

* * * *

What with assignments due in and exams to start preparing for, the next couple of weeks flew by, and the quiz night duly arrived, along with a stomach full of butterflies.

Ten tables of three had been set up on the large stage, each with a bell and a banner displaying the team name, whilst tables for spectators had been set out in the rest of the hall, with refreshments on sale at the back.

Mum and Dad came early with me, so were able to secure a table with a clear view of the stage.

Gradually the place filled up, and Mr Vernon, the college principal and tonight's quiz-master, asked all team members to take their seats.

"Our mascot," Suzie said, placing a furry starfish on our table.

"The Starmouth Starfish" was the only name we could think of at the time of registering our team.

Janice and her team took their places at "The Beauties" table. They certainly lived up to their name with their immaculate make-up, big hair, earrings and sparkly dresses.

The rest of us seemed dowdy in our comfy cords or jeans and T-shirts.

I noticed Declan glance at them once or twice – not that I was going to let that distract me.

Mr Vernon welcomed everyone to the event and wished all the contestants good luck before launching into round one.

"Who had a hit with 'Call Me' in February this year?"

Suzie's hand shot to the bell.

"Blondie."

We were off!

By the end of the first round, the teams were evenly matched, but differences started showing by the end of round three, with our team ahead by 10 points.

The picture round caused a wave of laughter when someone identified Burt Reynolds as Benny Hill.

In fairness, the pictures, courtesy of an overhead projector on a portable screen, weren't particularly sharp. I actually thought it was Russ Abbot in costume!

The gap between us and Janice's team narrowed rapidly when there were a few questions on fashion and art, and by the half-time break for refreshments we were five points behind.

"Stay calm, Jo," Suzie urged me as we were summoned back for the next half. "Focus on the questions, not on Janice."

"We can still do this," Declan reassured us. "There's plenty of time."

For the next few rounds, the lead pivoted between our team and Janice's, but a couple of the other teams were still in the running.

The final round came all too quickly.

I glanced at Mum, who put her thumbs up encouragingly.

We were two points behind the Beauties, but I was determined we were going to win.

We answered the next few questions correctly, but by the end of the round, with having been so focused on the questions, I'd completely lost track of the score.

Surely we'd done enough to win, hadn't we?

"At the end of that final round," Mr Vernon began, "we have a draw. That means we have a tie-break question between the Beauties and the Starfish."

I clutched the mascot, as if that was going to make all the difference, but Suzie snatched it away.

"Keep your hands free for the bell!"

"OK, here's the tie-breaker question," Mr Vernon said.

"And remember," he continued, turning to the audience and deliberately keeping everyone in suspense, "the team who answers it correctly will be the winners of the Starmouth College Quiz 1980."

There were cheers and whistles from the audience before everything fell silent again.

Mr Vernon held up the card with the question and began to read.

"What is the name of the pug in the stories of Rupert Bear?"

Really? My heart leapt and began racing.

I could feel Suzie and Declan's eyes boring into my head, and my mouth felt as if I'd just eaten a bowl of sawdust.

What was his name? I knew it!

It was Gregory! No, not Gregory.

The Beauties weren't ringing their bell.

Stewart Granger. Clark Gable. It's amazing the number of thoughts that can flash through your mind when you are under pressure, and how that second feels like an hour.

I glanced at Mum and Dad, who were sitting on the edge of their seats, staring at me open-mouthed.

Bulgy! It was something like Bulgy!

"We'll have to try another tie-breaker qu –"

"Algy," I shrieked as I pressed the bell, causing both Suzie and Declan to jump. "It's Algy, or Algernon, if you want his full name."

"Yes!" Mum and Dad both shouted together and practically jumped out of their chairs.

We'd done it!

Suzie and Declan hugged me as we accepted our trophy and had our photo taken for the local paper.

"For a minute I thought you weren't going to answer," Declan said afterwards.

"Just keeping everyone in suspense," I said nonchalantly.

"Congratulations, Jo."

I turned to see Janice standing there.

"Thanks. But it was just a lucky tie-breaker," I replied graciously. "It could have gone either way."

Janice smiled and I smiled back. In that moment, our rivalry ended.

"How brilliant was that!" Dad cried.

"Here's to one o'clock in the morning family arguments," I joked, much to Declan's puzzled amusement.

"I'll explain when you come round next time," I told him.

"That sounds good," he replied, smiling.

Never again would I feel awkward about my family's eccentricities. They were what made us special.

And although my mum and dad might have been older than other parents, they were young at heart and the most supportive family I could have wished for.

You could say that we were a winning team! ■

Starling

Shutterstock.

THE starlings' murmuration is a fascinating sight to behold. The collective aerial display can usually be seen in autumn – around sunset is the best time to spot them.

Thousands of these birds flock together and move and swirl in the sky as one mass of ever-changing shape.

With closer inspection, iridescent purple and green can be seen in starlings' feathers, although the female plumage is less vibrant.

You can spot them in most of the UK, aside from the Highlands.

Both male and female of the species help construct the nest and they tend to return to the same breeding ground, if not the same nest. They lay four to six pale blue eggs in each clutch.

While some may regard this bird as a pest, Mozart clearly thought otherwise, having had a starling as a pet which he was said to adore.

So much so that the composer penned a commemorative poem to his feathered friend upon its sad passing. ∎

Play On

by Val Bonsall

IT was my parents who got me going to guitar lessons, back when I was just entering my teens.

"It's something we've both always regretted, Michael, not learning to play a musical instrument," my mum explained.

So I was booked in with Mr Cross, who gave lessons from the huge old Victorian house where he lived with his wife.

I wasn't an enthusiastic pupil. Sport was more my thing.

But he was a kind and amiable man, popular locally for his involvement in community events, and I enjoyed the lessons a lot more than I had expected to.

Mrs Cross was nice, too. Clever. She worked in scientific research.

And though the imposing house was rather off-putting from the outside, inside it was wonderfully cosy.

It was September when I started, with the nights already drawing in.

I remember the room where we had our lessons, lamps aglow in every corner, bringing out the sheen on the piano in the big bay window.

Most of his pupils were for the piano or violin, but he did also have what looked to me to be a very good guitar.

He told me that when he was playing just for himself, when we'd all gone home, that was what he often turned to.

I had about half a dozen lessons, I suppose, before the half-term break, when we went away to visit family.

We came back home on Hallowe'en.

I considered myself to be rather old for running round the streets trick or treating, but I intended to go to the little party that Mr Cross, wearing his community hat, helped to organise every year.

It wasn't anything special. Sausages and music, plus witches cut out of black crepe paper adorning the walls of our equivalent of the village hall.

But it was popular, and there were a lot of people already there when I arrived.

Not Mr Cross, though.

I asked and found out that he'd sadly died while I'd been away.

I went the next day to see Mrs Cross.

She told me it was very sudden, but peaceful.

"He was in his music room. He'd written a song for the Hallowe'en do and was perfecting it."

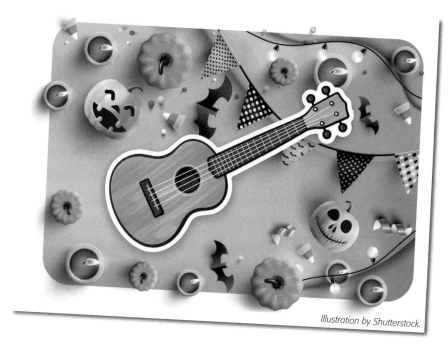

She smiled sadly.

"Truly, he went the way he would have wanted."

We were in the kitchen where she'd made us tea, but then she went into the music room and came back with his guitar.

"You were the only guitar pupil he had," she informed me, "so you take this, Mickey."

For some reason she always called me Mickey.

After a few polite refusals, I finally accepted it.

"Enjoy playing it," she said with a smile.

* * * *

I'm afraid I didn't enjoy playing it. I didn't play it at all.

I expected my parents to seek out a new teacher for me, but they didn't bother.

They'd decided while we were away on the half-term break to move house, and they were fully involved in that.

I didn't make any attempt myself, either.

I did keep the guitar, intending to return to it when I'd got used to my new life, in a new house, and in a new part of town.

But I never did.

When finally, several years later, I bought my own place, it moved there with me.

I thought that, propped up against a wall, it lent it a bohemian look to the under-furnished lounge.

But it was more than that, too, much more.

OK, I didn't play it, but it remained a treasured possession.

When I first moved in, a couple who knew Mrs Cross lived next door.

In fact, I'd heard about the house through Mrs Cross, with whom I'd continued to keep in touch.

They were lovely neighbours and I was sorry when they moved away.

To be honest, I was a bit wary when Lauren moved in with her two noisy young sons.

It didn't take me long to realise that Aaron, the younger of the pair, wasn't so bad.

But Ryan, in his early teens, was shaping up to be something of a headache to his mother, I suspected.

Which was a shame, because she was a nice woman and would have to deal with it on her own.

I'm not in the business of criticising either party to a marital break-up, but I'd heard from someone I worked with who knew Lauren that her husband had walked out and left them, after years of deceit.

Simple Joys

Often we are unaware
That simple joys are not that rare,
For here are just a few I know,
My very own portfolio.

A sunny day, a stunning view,
Music, whether old or new;
A listening ear that understands,
A walk together, holding hands.

A baby sharing its first smile,
Friends you've not seen in a while;
A book to read beside a fire,
A church with hymns sung by a choir.

These simple joys, however small
Can make life brighter for us all.

John Darley

"I reckon that's when Ryan went off the rails," my colleague confided, before adding that she suspected the ex-husband wasn't too good at providing financial support for his sons.

One day I saw Lauren outside a charity shop near where we lived.

She was assessing a guitar in the window. It was just a few quid and had a couple of "Teach Yourself" books thrown in with it.

"Taking up music?" I asked her, glad to stop and talk. I liked Lauren.

"Ryan has said he fancies learning to play," she explained. "I'm keen to encourage him."

I agreed it was a good idea.

But as we were standing there, one of the volunteer assistants lifted the instrument from the window and handed it to a customer.

Beaten to the post.

"I used to have a guitar," I told Lauren.

I was meaning the one my parents had bought for me when I started with Mr Cross.

"Unfortunately, I chucked it out," I added.

But you still have Mr Cross's guitar, a voice from inside reminded me. Yes, I replied to myself, but I could never give that away.

* * * *

All evening I thought about it.

I didn't use Mr Cross's guitar. It reminded me of a lovely man, yes, but I wouldn't forget him anyway. The years had shown me that.

And Mr Cross had always tried to help people.

So, if giving his guitar to Ryan helped the lad see a better way of using his time, then surely Mr Cross would have been pleased.

"I could even say to Ryan," I said to myself as I reached for my jacket, "that if he didn't take to it, he should let me have the guitar back."

I was going to call on Mrs Cross. This wasn't something I'd do without her agreement.

On the way I almost got cold feet about raising the topic, but when we were sitting in what had been the music room, I just came out with it.

She replied immediately that I should pass on the guitar to Ryan.

She looked at a framed photo of Mr Cross.

"Clint always said it should be played," she added with a smile.

* * * *

Well, Ryan certainly played it. As the guy living in the adjoining house, I could fully attest to that!

"He's not disturbing you, is he?" Lauren constantly asked me.

"Not at all."

He wasn't, not really.

"And when I do hear him," I told her, "it's a pleasure. He's getting good at it."

"He is, isn't he? He's really keen. He even got himself a paper round to help pay for his lessons."

Lauren smiled.

"It's really saved him, getting this new interest. He'd joined a bad crowd, probably in reaction to all the disruption we had," she confided. "But he's back now."

I nodded. I could see the change in him.

"He's going to play at that Hallowe'en charity event they have every year," she continued.

"His first public performance! Will you be there?"

"Of course," I replied.

I phoned Mrs Cross and told her how well it was going.

"I don't always bother with the Hallowe'en thing," she said, "but I'll come along this year to hear him for myself."

* * * *

We all arrived around the same time: me and Mrs Cross, Lauren, Aaron and Ryan.

The event always did well for the charity, but was famed for being rather chaotic, and this year was no exception.

Jacket potatoes that should have been ready weren't, as no-one had thought to switch the huge oven on.

Cobweb decorations that had been pinned to the ceiling came falling down, causing much mock-screaming.

I felt sorry for the various musicians who were providing the entertainment.

At times there was so much noise – good-humoured, admittedly – that they could barely be heard.

Seeing Ryan standing at the side of the stage, awaiting his call, I went over to him to offer my support and help calm his nerves.

In fact, he didn't seem one bit anxious.

I suggested he play songs everyone knew, so people could join in with him since no-one would be seriously listening.

"Maybe later," he replied. "I want to start off with a song I've written myself."

I wasn't hopeful about that, I had to admit.

But as soon as he started playing this song of his own, the whole room went quiet.

The word "power" came to my mind. It had a power.

I turned to Mrs Cross and got a shock. Her face was as white as the cut-out ghost pinned up behind her.

"That song," she whispered to me. "It's Clint's, Mickey."

"He'd just got it as he wanted it and was playing it when he died."

*　　*　　*　　*

I don't know if Ryan did finish his session with well-known hits, as I'd recommended.

I couldn't concentrate on anything for the rest of the evening.

We talked about it as I walked home with Mrs Cross along the dark streets.

"It did sound like Clint's song at first," she told me, "but it must just have been a few notes that were the same. They caught my attention."

"It does happen," I agreed. "You read about court cases where some band sues another because they say they've copied their song, but the other party totally deny it."

"Yes." She nodded. "It happens in science, too. You're working on something you believe is entirely new, then you discover the same experiments are being conducted elsewhere."

We stepped aside briefly to allow two skeletons, holding hands and taking up half the pavement, to pass us.

"I guess," Mrs Cross resumed, "since we're all subject to the same input in our daily lives, we get to thinking the same way.

"Maybe Ryan also experienced whatever it was that inspired Clint and it inspired him, too."

She continued with her theory. She was clever at that sort of thing.

But I wasn't properly listening, thinking back to what she'd said when I'd visited her to discuss giving Ryan the guitar.

"Clint always said it should be played . . ." ■

Everything Changes

by Alyson Hilbourne

NURSE NORA TULLOCH ducked her head to get out of the Anderson shelter and blinked into the daylight.

The family in front of her were blocking the stairs.

Nora coughed politely and they shuffled forward.

With a clearer view of the street, Nora understood their surprise.

Dust hung in the air like bonfire smoke on a still day. It caught in Nora's throat and made her cough.

Through the haze she saw a scene of devastation.

The terraced houses on one side of the road had been ripped apart, leaving a gap in the middle like a missing tooth.

Bricks, timbers and glass had been strewn across the cobbles.

The mansion block on the corner had had all its windows blown out, and blackout curtains were flapping from the gaps.

It was eerily quiet, with people emerging like rabbits from different shelters and trying to take it all in.

Nora blinked again, trying to make sense of the sight in front of her.

She had been on her way home from her shift at the infirmary when the air-raid siren had caught her out.

She'd followed people into the nearest shelter and spent the night with her eyes tight shut, jumping as vibrations shook the shelter.

The docks were the likely target, but it sounded as if the whole town was being blasted to oblivion.

Even when the explosions faded away, a child's whimpering, the mother's shushing and an old man's constant throat-clearing had kept everyone in the shelter awake.

Nora's eyes were gritty with tiredness as she emerged into the light.

A couple of ARP wardens were searching the wrecked house, clambering over the piles of rubble.

Illustration by Gerard Fay.

The first workmen of the day were walking towards the docks, carrying their gas masks and lunch cans.

Nora set out towards home. She wouldn't have long before she was on duty again.

She heard a scream, followed by sobbing from one of the terraced houses with broken windows.

She hurried towards the noise and peered in the broken window.

A woman lay on the floor inside.

"Hello!" Nora called.

"Oh, help. Please, help!" The woman gasped.

It was dark inside the living-room, but Nora could make out the woman's pale face and wide eyes.

"Are you hurt? Can you get up?" Nora asked.

The woman gasped and clutched at her stomach, and at that moment Nora realised she was heavily pregnant and in labour.

"I'm coming," she told her and stepped towards the door.

She tried the handle, but the door wouldn't budge.

She glanced around. She might be taken for a burglar.

At that moment a young man in fireman's uniform approached.

"Can you help?" Nora asked. "There's a woman inside in labour. I need to get in."

The fireman wore a dark jacket with brass buttons, boots and a tin helmet.

His face and uniform were streaked with dirt, and from his slow gait and slumped shoulders Nora guessed he'd been on duty all night.

A pair of wire-framed glasses rested crookedly on his nose. They gave him a slightly owlish appearance.

He gestured Nora out of the way.

"Let me try," he said, and launched his shoulder into the door.

"The blasts might have shifted the frame."

There was a splintering sound as the door burst open, and Nora hurried inside, leaving the fireman checking the lock and the hinges.

She took off her coat, revealing her uniform, and pushed up her sleeves.

"It's all right," she said, kneeling down beside the woman. "I can help."

The woman grasped her hand, nearly crushing the bones.

"Don't leave me." She sobbed. "I'm so frightened."

"There's no need to be scared," Nora assured her, more calmly than she felt. "A baby is the most natural thing in the world."

She'd been with women in labour before, but had never birthed a baby on her own.

She squeezed the woman's hand.

"Of course I won't leave you," she added.

She was pleased, however, when the fireman stepped into the room. It felt as if the burden was shared.

"Sorry." Tears ran down the woman's face. "I couldn't get to the shelter. I heard the planes coming over . . ."

"Have you been in labour all night?" Nora asked, chewing her lip.

"Yes." The woman shuddered as another contraction ran through her. "It's getting worse."

"Well, my name is Nora Tulloch and I'm a nurse at the infirmary," Nora said. "And this is . . ."

She glanced up at the fireman who stood over them. He looked rather pale as he pushed his glasses up his nose.

"Harold Dean. Fireman," he mumbled.

"See," Nora soothed the woman. "We're both here to help.

"Harold, can you find some clean water and towels of some sort?"

He turned and hurried off with some speed as another contraction gripped the woman and she doubled up.

"Here, put this cushion under your head. That will help," Nora said, moving the cushion from the settee with one hand as the woman still gripped her other hand. "What's your name?"

"Mary Pitts. My husband is in France. He was going to get leave."

When Harold came back with a bowl of water and some towels, Nora set him to wiping Mary's brow with a damp cloth as she attended to the delivery.

Mary screamed and pushed.

Harold gripped her hand, whispering to her all the time.

"It'll be fine," he said. "Is it a boy or a girl you want?"

Mary panted replies to him between the contractions, and Nora was glad he was keeping her distracted.

She was pleased when she could see the baby's head crowning, and then, with one final scream, a small wrinkled body was in Nora's hands.

She rubbed it down, checked its airways and wrapped it up in a towel.

"A lovely boy!" she told Mary.

Harold rocked back on his knees as Nora laid the baby on Mary's chest.

A while later, as Nora tidied up, Harold made them tea.

They were grinning at each other, all trace of tiredness gone in the excitement of the safe delivery.

Nora had to pinch herself. She'd delivered a baby!

She helped Mary get the baby to nurse, then watched with tears in her eyes as its thin eyelids, as delicate as dragonfly wings, fluttered in delight and a tiny hand with tiny fingernails gripped the top of the towel.

A morning that had started in disaster had become one of wonder and excitement as everything changed.

* * * *

Almost 50 years later, Nora stood in her living-room with the same feelings of disbelief and concern as she'd had that morning when she'd stepped out of the Anderson shelter.

She didn't know how she was going to get through the next few hours.

She swallowed and tried to clear the lump that had lodged in her throat. Then she wiped her eyes with the back of her hand.

She straightened the photographs on the mantelpiece.

In pride of place was the fading snap of Harold and herself on their wedding day at the end of the war.

Harold wore his fireman's uniform and she had a dress made of parachute silk lent to her by a friend.

Between them, clutching a small posy of flowers and looking very pleased with himself, was three-year-old Harold Pitts.

Mary Pitts had named the baby after Harold.

"I'd have called it after you, love, if it had been a girl," she'd told Nora.

Nora and Harold had kept in touch and continued to visit Mary and the baby.

When they got married, Mary and Little Harold were guests of honour. They had supported Mary when her husband was reported missing and then declared dead.

Little Harold often came to stay with them, and when it seemed they would not have children of their own he became a surrogate child.

Harold taught Little Harold to swim on day trips to the beach.

Nora taught him to make cakes when she could get sugar and butter.

They helped celebrate his birthdays and, best of all, they had been there when Little Harold had joined the fire brigade and begun working at the same station as Harold.

Nora touched another photograph. They had been at Little Harold's wedding, and visited the hospital when his daughters, Claire and Sarah, had been born.

"More traditional start than I had," Little Harold had joked as Nora tucked a teddy bear into the corner of Claire's cot.

Now Claire was married, too, to yet another fireman.

More tears welled up in Nora's eyes as she looked at the photos.

She was lost in the memories when a sharp knock at the door sent her hurrying out to the hall.

"Harold!" she cried, opening the door. "Don't you look smart?"

Little Harold, no longer so little, stood in his uniform, helmet tucked under his arm.

"Ready, Nora?" he asked softly.

She gave a quick nod, tweaked her black dress and picked up her handbag.

Then she stood straight and followed Little Harold out of the house, pulling the door shut behind her.

Harold helped her into the black car. They sat together in the back seat as it drove to the fire station.

Parked on the forecourt was a sparkling red tender already loaded with her Harold's coffin, heaped with white flowers and a huge wreath.

Firemen jumped up on to the running boards as the car drew up.

Nora looked out of the window as their car followed the fire engine. People had lined the streets.

Most respectfully bowed their heads, but the odd few clapped.

The car drove round by the docks, now a huge marina with expensive yachts and large speedboats moored against wooden quays.

They drove down the road where Little Harold had been born.

The terraced houses were long gone, and glass and steel flats had been built overlooking the water.

It had all changed, Nora thought.

When the fire tender got to the church, firemen formed a guard of honour along the path, and eight more carried Harold's coffin inside.

"Harold was respected and loved by everyone at the station," Little Harold said as Nora stifled a sob.

Harold had stayed in the fire brigade after the war and worked his way up to be station commander before his retirement.

Various local dignitaries paid tribute to him through the funeral service, but best of all for Nora was Little Harold's tribute to the father he'd never had.

Half an hour later they left the church together.

Nora's throat was dry and her eyes were scratchy. She blinked at the daylight after the dark inside the church.

As she looked around, trying to make sense of things, a hand slipped into hers and squeezed.

"We're here, Auntie Nora," Little Harold's daughter Claire said.

Little Harold's wife, Alice, closed in on the other side and pressed against her.

Claire's husband hovered in the background and Sarah stood beside Little Harold.

Nora smiled round at her surrogate family.

"Everything is changing," she remarked.

"It is," Claire agreed gently. "And Auntie Nora, it's going to change even more, because we're expecting a baby!"

Nora looked up at her with watery eyes.

"That's wonderful, Claire. Wonderful!"

Life would continue to go on. Dear Harold might be gone, but she still had many wonderful people to share it with. ∎

Kingfisher

Shutterstock.

I**F** you're lucky enough to have a river near your house, then keep your eyes peeled for a common kingfisher.

It's the only native kind in the UK, though scarcer in Scotland.

The beautiful vibrant blue hue of its plumage is contrasted with underparts in orange, with both males and females having the same colour plumage. Only the beak colour differs.

Kingfishers lay around half a dozen eggs in steep sandy banks.

The breeding pair take turns to burrow a tunnel to create a nesting chamber at the end in which to lay the eggs, and both males and females incubate them.

The young eat upwards of a dozen minnows or sticklebacks daily.

These birds also eat insects and tadpoles, diving headfirst with wings outstretched into the water to catch their meal, though they cannot swim. The adults eat their own bodyweight in fish each day!

Kingfishers have a high-pitched trill and are very territorial. ■

The Empty Chair

by Glenda Young

I N Poland, on Christmas Eve, it's traditional to set an extra plate at the table and leave an empty chair when you sit down to eat."

Bronwyn was surprised to hear this and intrigued to learn more, but she didn't dare take her concentration off the road.

The snow was coming down heavily and her windscreen wipers worked furiously against the driving blanket of white.

As her red estate car inched along the motorway, she could just about make out the blue sign ahead.

With a sigh of relief, she flicked her left indicator and began to ease the car into the slip lane.

"This is the turning for the airport, Pavel," she explained. "We should be there soon.

"It's going to be busy with it being Christmas Eve and everyone trying to get home. Are you sure you don't need me to come inside with you?"

"I'm quite sure, thank you," Pavel replied.

"Well, as long as you're sure. I'll drop you at the short-term car park."

She nervously checked her rear-view mirror, but all she could see were headlights in the snow.

She turned her head to look through the windows, taking time to manoeuvre her car slowly and carefully between lanes.

A car horn honked behind her. She gripped the steering wheel.

It was almost impossible to see.

Had she been in danger of hitting another car or was the driver letting her know it was safe to pull out?

She couldn't tell through the snow; she could barely see a thing.

Finally, with a sigh of relief, she was now on the slip road where the traffic was much lighter.

"How are we doing for time?" she asked, keeping her eyes firmly on the road ahead.

Pavel checked his watch.

"We have over three hours before my plane leaves. I'm grateful to you

Illustration by Sarah Holliday.

for taking me to the airport, and in such dreadful weather, too."

"It's the least I can do for you. After living with us for the last six months, it feels like you're part of our family now," Bronwyn replied.

It was true. Pavel had settled into Bronwyn's family life from the moment he'd arrived in England.

Bronwyn and her husband, Paul, often took in overseas students who were studying at the nearby university.

The students were sent on exchange programmes, and Pavel's course in chemistry had lasted for six months.

As an alternative to living in student accommodation, the university was keen for their overseas students to stay with local families who could offer a rounded experience of English family life.

Since Pavel had arrived at Bronwyn's home, he'd fitted in like a dream.

He was funny, intelligent, keen to improve his English language skills and, to Bronwyn's delight, he was even helpful around the house.

He always insisted on doing the washing up each night, and taught their five-year-old son, Andrew, some basic Polish words, too.

Andrew thought the world of Pavel, and the two had become close.

In fact, Andrew treated Pavel like a big brother and had been in tears that morning when they'd said their final goodbye.

There had been tears in Pavel's eyes, too.

Paul, stoic to the end, had given Pavel a firm handshake, but she had seen his lip quiver, and she knew he'd miss Pavel a lot.

After Bronwyn had assured Paul that she'd drive safely through the snow, Paul set off in his own car to drop Andrew at his mum's before heading to work for the last day before the Christmas break.

Bronwyn followed the signs to the airport, relieved that the snow was starting to ease.

She felt less nervous now, but knew she had to be careful as more snow was forecast and the sky hung heavy and grey.

She drove more slowly and carefully than she'd ever done in her life.

The snow had settled on the dual carriageway that led to the airport and was now a few inches deep.

She had to keep the car wheels from slipping.

She followed a car in front, its red tail lights shining like a warning.

"This weather is dreadful," she muttered.

"This is nothing compared to snow storms at home," Pavel remarked.

Bronwyn eased her foot off the pedal as the car ahead slowed to stop at traffic lights.

She quickly glanced at Pavel.

"What was that you were saying about an empty chair?" she asked.

Pavel's face lit up with a smile.

"In my country, it is a tradition on Christmas Eve to prepare an extra chair and set a plate at the table for the evening meal."

"What for?" she asked.

"In case there is an unexpected visitor," Pavel explained. "Each family leaves an empty chair at the table in case there is a knock at the door from someone who needs a meal."

"That sounds incredibly generous," Bronwyn replied.

The car ahead began to move and she changed gear, then gripped the steering wheel as her car inched forward again.

A sign ahead, covered with snow, said the airport was two miles away.

"Does your family always set an extra plate on Christmas Eve?" she asked.

"Oh, yes." Pavel nodded. "Most people in Poland do, and we eat carp on Christmas Eve, too. It's another Polish tradition."

Bronwyn nodded.

"Carp? And has anyone unexpected ever turned up at your door?"

Pavel shook his head.

"No, but the plate and the chair are always ready. In fact, my *matka* always prays that someone might arrive."

Pavel's hand flew to his mouth as if to take his words back.

Bronwyn shot Pavel a concerned look.

"Your *matka*? That's your mother, right?"

Pavel leaned back in his seat and glanced out of the window, turning his head from Bronwyn.

Slowly, he began to speak.

"It is this weather; it is making me homesick, I think. I am very much looking forward to seeing Matka again."

"I'm sure your *matka* and your *ojciec* will be excited to see you," Bronwyn added, remembering the Polish word for father.

"Sorry, I have said too much," Pavel said quickly.

Bronwyn drove slowly past another sign for the airport that said it was now just one mile away.

"I'm sorry. I wasn't prying," she said.

There was silence for a few moments until Pavel began to speak.

"My *ojciec*, he . . ." Pavel paused. "He argued with my older brother Tomasz a few years ago on Christmas Eve.

"Tomasz stormed out and refused to return. He went to live in Warsaw and we haven't seen him since."

Bronwyn's heart went out to the boy.

"I'm so sorry," she said.

Pavel patted his jeans pocket where he kept his phone.

"I keep in touch with Tomasz and we text all the time. But life was difficult at home.

"My brother and father are too much alike – hot-headed."

Bronwyn saw the sign ahead for the airport car park and felt a lump rise in her throat.

After six months of Pavel living with her family, she could hardly bring herself to admit he was leaving for good and she'd never see him again.

She knew she shouldn't get attached to the students they took in, but Pavel had been different, sensitive and caring, and she knew that she'd miss him just as Andrew and Paul would, too.

She pulled the car into the drop-off area in the short-term car park.

"Let me help you with your suitcase," she said, but Pavel, polite to the end, insisted on getting it himself from the boot.

Bronwyn opened the car window, and Pavel leaned towards her and kissed her on both cheeks.

"Thank you for all you have done for me," he said. "I have never felt more at home than when I was with you all."

Bronwyn saw tears in his eyes and felt like her heart would burst.

"Travel safely, Pavel," she said, her voice breaking.

She touched her hand to her phone in the hands-free holder on the dashboard.

"Keep in touch."

Bronwyn watched as Pavel wheeled his suitcase away and disappeared through the automatic doors.

"Come on, Bronwyn, pull yourself together," she told herself.

Then she put her car into gear and slowly drove out to join the snow-covered road to the motorway.

✳   ✳   ✳   ✳

That evening, Bronwyn set the table for their Christmas Eve meal of golden, crispy fish and chips, which Paul had bought on his way home from work.

There were four chairs at the table, but only three of them sitting down to eat.

A thought came to Bronwyn and she took another plate from the cupboard with another knife and fork.

"Not expecting anyone else, are we?" Paul asked, puzzled.

Bronwyn explained the Polish tradition that Pavel had told her about.

"I miss Pavel." Andrew frowned.

Bronwyn ruffled her son's hair and exchanged a look with Paul.

"We all miss Pavel," she replied.

When the food was on their plates, tea poured and bread buttered, there was a knock at the door.

"I'll get it," Paul said, standing up.

Bronwyn sat down and helped Andrew cut his fish into small bites.

A few moments later, Bronwyn couldn't believe her eyes when Pavel walked through the door.

"My flight was cancelled," Pavel explained. "The snow is too bad. I have called Matka to let her know.

"May I stay until the day after tomorrow, when the flight will try again?"

"Of course you can stay!" Paul said firmly, patting Pavel on the shoulder.

"Pavel!" Andrew cried, banging his knife and fork on the table.

Pavel eyed the food on the table.

"I'm sorry, I don't want to intrude on your Christmas Eve meal."

"Nonsense," Bronwyn told him. "Your plate is set and the seat is empty. I set a place for the unexpected guest you told me about."

Pavel's eyes opened wide.

"Thank you," he said.

Bronwyn filled his plate with fish and chips shared from her own and Paul's plates.

She filled a mug of tea for him and handed over the plate of bread.

"It's cod, not carp, but I think you'll like it all the same." She smiled.

Pavel took his coat off and put his rucksack down.

Then his phone beeped. He pulled it from his pocket, swiped the screen and stared at it open-mouthed.

He sank into the empty seat and slowly turned his phone so that Bronwyn could see the screen.

"Matka has sent a photograph. See? She set a place at the table and left an empty chair for the unexpected guest.

"Look who turned up," he said softly.

Bronwyn looked at the screen.

There was a beautiful woman with dark hair that she recognised as Pavel's mother. Next to her was a proud-looking man.

"My father," Pavel explained.

"And this person?" Bronwyn asked, pointing at a young man in the centre of the screen.

Pavel choked back a tear.

"It's Tomasz. He's home at last." ■

Ballater, Aberdeenshire

Once owned by the Knights of St John, helpers of pilgrims making their way to and from Europe's holy shrines, this picturesque area of Aberdeenshire has been a popular spot for visitors for centuries.

In addition to the beautiful scenery formed by long-ago glaciers, people flocked to take the waters at the Pannanich mineral well. The healing powers were said to cure all kinds of ailments. Lord Byron and Sir Walter Scott were among the well's famous visitors.

The town of Ballater grew up to serve the increasing numbers who travelled to the well. By 1838 it was being recommended in tourist guides to Scotland. Comparing it with Aberdeen, one guide said, "As for pleasantness and agreeableness, everyone must admit that Ballater has the advantage, else why do such numbers of Aberdeen people leave their homes there and come out here every summer to take up their abode – while few or none of the Ballater people ever visit Aberdeen except on urgent business?"

When Queen Victoria visited, she fell in love with the town and its environs. Prince Albert bought Balmoral Castle for her in 1852, and she wrote fondly about her connection to the area in her diaries, calling it her "dear paradise in the Highlands".

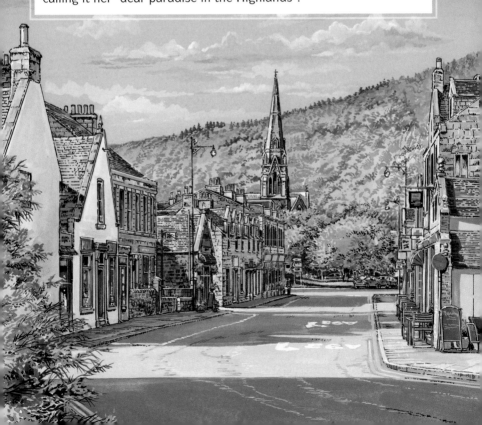

The Angel's Gift

by Rosemary Gemmell

"MUMMY, I don't want to be an angel! Only girls are meant to be angels."

It was the daily refrain when six-year-old Ben returned from school. Miriam had tried to reassure her son.

"The Angel Gabriel was a man, and many others. In fact, I don't know any girls who were real angels."

Ben's little world revolved around his primary school, and especially the forthcoming nativity play.

How many homes were in turmoil in the lead-up to the Christmas play each year? Yet she assumed none of the parents would want to miss the opportunity to see their child on stage.

It was two years since Ben's dad died and Miriam missed him every day. Thankfully, her illustration work was beginning to bring in commissions, and she could work from home to be there for Ben.

Now Ben was upset at being an angel, while his friend, Jacob, was playing Joseph.

She would need to have a word with Ben's teacher, Mr Johnson. She had met him briefly when Ben started his new class.

Mr Johnson seemed pleased enough to see her, leaving the class with the assistant while he spoke to Miriam in the corridor.

"What seems to be the problem, Mrs Collins?" he asked. "Ben is usually a happy little boy, but I gather something is bothering him?"

Miriam appreciated his gentle but firm demeanour and kind brown eyes, instinctively reassured he was good with the young children.

"I'm afraid it's the nativity play. Ben's not happy at being an angel."

The side of his mouth quirked when he answered.

"Ah, I see. I thought he wasn't bringing his usual enthusiasm."

Miriam waited for his solution, but he seemed to be waiting for her to continue.

"I don't suppose anything can be done about it?" she asked.

"All the parts are assigned now," Mr Johnson replied. "I thought Ben deserved a main part as he has a good speaking voice."

"Oh." She hadn't thought of it like that. "I don't understand. Aren't there lots of angels?"

"Yes, several of the girls are angels, but Ben has two lines."

By the end of the conversation Miriam was only slightly reassured, but she was impressed by Mr Johnson – or Matthew, as he insisted.

"I'll make sure Ben is fine with his part by the end of rehearsals," he assured her.

* * * *

Miriam still had to convince Ben that he had a special part to play.

The next day, Ben rushed out of school in tears, and her heart plummeted further.

"Did something happen at school today?" Miriam asked him gently once they were home.

"Jacob said everyone's bringing a gift to the baby Jesus except the angels." Ben sobbed. "And he was right."

As if being an angel wasn't bad enough, now Ben had another issue. Miriam could only tell him what Mr Johnson had said.

"I spoke to your teacher, and he told me that angels are very special.

"They were messengers. They told the shepherds what would happen.

"Maybe I could ask to watch you practising the play," she suggested as an afterthought.

Ben's face broke into a wide smile.

"Yes! Could you, Mummy?"

Miriam hoped it was possible, but her suggestion was worth it to see Ben's face happy again.

Miriam phoned the school and asked to speak to Mr Johnson.

There was silence for a moment before he spoke.

"I don't see why not. Can you pop in at lunchtime?"

Relieved to be doing something that might help Ben, Miriam changed from the old leggings and shirt that she wore for painting, convincing herself it was to give her confidence, rather than the thought of impressing anyone.

Since she was between commissions, she'd started a sketch for a picture book of her own, inspired by the problem of the angel's gift.

Perhaps the rehearsal would provide more ideas.

The wave of noise hit her when she was directed to the school hall. Used to the silence of her work space, she wondered how anyone could cope with a class full of noisy six-year-olds.

Keeping to the back, Miriam finally noticed Ben beside Jacob.

Then he turned and saw her, his face lighting up.

Miriam was soon smiling at the sweet antics of the children as they tried to follow their teacher's instructions.

Between the noisy "baas" of sheep and the "moos" of cows, several girls pranced about the stage, flapping their arms for angels' wings.

Ben, however, stood looking at the floor, seeming lost.

Miriam's heart went out to him and she wanted to jump up on stage to reassure him.

She was relieved when Mr Johnson turned his attention to Ben.

"Now for the important angel's words. Ready, Ben?"

Ben sent Miriam a quick glance, then he nodded.

Standing in front of the shepherds, the other angels spread out beside him, Ben gave them his message.

"Don't be afraid. Go and see the special baby, born in a manger."
Miriam's heart swelled at Ben's strong voice.

She was full of admiration that Mr Johnson managed to get the children to the manger scene without serious incident.

Soon, all the cast gathered around Mary and Joseph and baby Jesus. She took a deep breath and waited for Ben's final line.

Standing in front, he lifted his arms and spoke, then took his place beside the other children.

She saw Mr Johnson pat Ben's shoulder before he left the children with his assistant for a moment and made his way towards her.

"I hope it wasn't too noisy for you, Mrs Collins. Ben did very well."

"I loved it, though you must have a lot of patience to coach them."

"Believe me, it's in short supply sometimes."

His grin belied his words. These children were very fortunate to have such a teacher.

"I'm afraid I have to get on now, but I'd love to chat more about Ben. Would you like to have a coffee with me some time?"

"I think I could manage that. Can I call you?" Miriam replied.

It was hard to concentrate that afternoon, though it was nothing to do with Ben, for a change.

Well, perhaps indirectly. She liked Matthew Johnson, much as she wanted to deny it.

Steven had been the love of her life and she was still not over his sudden death.

Yet more than one well-meaning friend had pointed out that she was young enough to find love again.

*　*　*　*

Ben couldn't wait to talk about the play when he got home.

"Did you like it, Mummy? Was I a good angel?"

"It was wonderful, Ben, and you were the most important angel on the stage. I can't wait to see everyone dressed up."

His face fell as he frowned.

"But I don't want to wear glittery tinsel like the girls!"

Miriam thought carefully before answering.

"Maybe there's a different way you could be all shiny and important. I'll speak to Mr Johnson about it."

Arguing with herself all day as to why it was a bad idea to meet with Matthew, she eventually dialled his number.

"I am glad you called, Miriam," he said. "Saturday is perfect. Why don't we meet at the café in town?"

Having dropped Ben off at Jacob's house, Miriam spent the whole afternoon trying to find something to wear.

She needn't have worried. As soon as they started chatting, it was as if they'd known each other for years.

She discovered Matthew had never been married, but had come close before the girl had gone to the other side of the world.

"I realised I didn't love her enough to go with her," Matthew said.

"Ben must miss his father. Not to mention your own loss."

"It was hard, but he is doing well now. Although he'll miss having a dad as he grows up, I expect," Miriam explained.

Matthew nodded.

"I can understand that. I lost my own father very young."

Miriam looked at him in surprise.

"Oh, I'm sorry to hear that."

"And yes, it was tough losing my husband, but I try to keep things as normal as possible for Ben's sake."

"I'm sure you're doing a wonderful job. He's a happy little guy and I want him to appreciate his special part in the play."

She mentioned Ben's worry about a gift for the baby, as well as how to make him shine without glitter and tinsel.

"I have an idea," Matthew replied. "How about if we create plenty of light around Ben so he really shines?"

Miriam was shocked at how quickly the time had gone in and how much she had enjoyed adult conversation again.

* * * *

As December darkened into long, cosy winter nights, Miriam managed to get through the illustrations for her book idea.

It was a simple version of the Nativity story for very young children.

She was enjoying drawing all the main characters, then making their clothes as colourful as possible.

Mary's dress was a deep ultramarine blue-purple, while Joseph's simple long tunic was a burnt umber rather than a washed-out brown.

The shepherds had stripes of orange, ochre yellow and grass green.

Young children wouldn't care about the authenticity of colours, but would love the bright highlights.

As she was painting the glittery wings of the angels, Miriam gave the central angel a good likeness of Ben's face.

She stared at it for a while, trying to imagine how a special messenger would shine, then she filled her brush with lemon yellow paint.

Sitting back some time later, she smiled.

Another phone call to Matthew was needed to see if he liked her idea for Ben's costume.

He seemed pleased to hear from her when she phoned the next day.

"That sounds good," he told her. "Why don't you come by the school and bring me your drawing?"

Miriam hesitated, not entirely sure she was doing the right thing.

"I have a better idea. Would you like to come here for dinner with me and Ben? We can talk about it once Ben is in bed."

He was quick to agree and Miriam spent the rest of the day worrying that she had made a mistake in inviting him to her home.

But Ben's reaction more than made up for any misgivings.

"Mr Johnson's coming here?" he cried. "Brilliant!"

It was a huge success, and Ben agreed to go to bed only if Matthew would read him a story.

Once Ben was settled, Miriam made coffee for herself and Matthew.

"Thank you for everything," she said. "You've made Ben's day."

"You should be very proud of him – and yourself."

Miriam sipped her coffee to avoid Matthew's gaze.

"Do you think my idea might work?" she asked at last.

"May I see your drawing, please?"

Matthew turned each page without speaking, right to the end.

"You have such a great talent, Miriam. I can see Ben dressed like this."

After some more discussion about art and teaching, he stood to leave.

"Thank you for a lovely evening, Miriam."

A sudden panic at how to say goodnight made her take a step back.

"It was a pleasure. Thanks again for coming."

Matthew smiled, but didn't come any closer.

"See you at the play." Then he was gone.

*　*　*　*

When the day of the play approached, Miriam nervously took her seat with all the other parents, hoping she had reassured Ben enough over the last few days.

She smiled with everyone else at the antics of one little angel who only wanted to dance with her glittery wings flapping.

Her heart melted at the serious children playing Mary and Joseph.

Then it was Ben's turn, and she sat up anxiously.

As the shepherds sat down with their toy sheep, there was a gasp as Ben glided on to the stage dressed in a long lemon-yellow tunic, huge white wings at the back, and a large halo adorned with shiny silver stars.

As he delivered his line so that the audience could hear, Miriam swelled with pride.

At the end of the play, the lights dimmed and Ben took his place at the front.

This time, lights illuminated his part of the stage as he said his words.

"And the glory of the Lord shone around."

As Ben took his place beside the others and they all sang "Away In A Manger", Miriam wasn't the only parent positively glowing with joy.

*　*　*　*

It was much later when Ben finally agreed it was time for bed.

"I know what the angel's gift was, Mummy. Mr Johnson told me."

"What was that, Ben?" Miriam asked.

"It was light! There was no electricity at that time, so the shiny angel brought the light to the baby Jesus."

Miriam hugged into her son as she wished him goodnight.

Ben was right – in more ways than one.

She would still need a lot of time, and she had no idea where her friendship with Matthew might eventually lead, but she did know one thing.

Matthew, too, had brought a gift of light into their world this Christmas, and given her hope for the future. ■

Clun Valley, Shropshire.

The rural idyll of Clun Valley has the highest concentration of watercourses throughout the Shropshire Hills. Not surprisingly, it is an Area of Outstanding Natural Beauty. It is also peaceful – this area is one of the most sparsely populated in England.

The peace, however, is deceptive. This was one of the most fought-over territories in ancient times. The border country between England and Wales remained unsettled for centuries.

Offa, King of Mercia, attempted to define it in the eighth century by commanding a vast earthwork to delineate the frontier from north to south. Some 20 metres wide and rising up to 2.4 metres high, this formidable earthwork was an amazing achievement for the people who constructed it long before mechanised equipment.

It didn't stop the fighting, though, and was rigorously defended. Legend has it that anyone emerging from the Welsh side stood at risk of having a hand or an ear cut off!

However, tranquillity now prevails and today's visitors can expect a much warmer welcome!